A MARRIAGE MANUAL

FOR CATHOLICS

A

Marriage Manual

FOR

CATHOLICS

By William A. Lynch, M.D.

WITH A FOREWORD BY HIS EMINENCE

Richard Cardinal Cushing

TRIDENT PRESS, NEW YORK

1964

The Marriage Service and the Mass for the Bridegroom and Bride are
from *The New Roman Missal* by Rev. F. X. Lasance and Rev. Francis A.
Walsh, O.S.B., copyright 1956 by Benziger Brothers, Inc. The Betrothal
Rite is from *Roman Ritual* by Rev. Philip Weller, copyright 1946 by
The Bruce Publishing Company. They are reprinted with the publishers'
permission.

NIHIL OBSTAT: James A. O'Donohoe
                Diocesan Censor

IMPRIMATUR: ✠ Richard Cardinal Cushing
               Archbishop of Boston

March 17, 1964
Boston, Massachusetts

ACKNOWLEDGMENTS

I would like to pay tribute to the interest shown by all those who have had a part in the preparation of this book and to gratefully acknowledge their kind assistance. I wish to acknowledge my gratitude to the Archbishop of Boston, Richard Cardinal Cushing, for his encouragement and, in particular, for his kindness in supplying the Foreword to this work. His Excellency, the Most Reverend Thomas J. Riley, Auxiliary Bishop of Boston, was most gracious and helpful throughout the project. I am particularly grateful to the Reverend James O'Donohoe for reading the manuscript and for his suggestions and corrections; to Right Reverend Monsignor Francis J. Sexton, Vice-Chancellor of the Archdiocese of Boston, for his interest and help in many, many ways; to the Reverend Edward J. Gorman, S.J., for his help in assessing the original crude material and for a thousand friendly things; to the Reverend Robert J. Hudson, C.S.Sp., for his generous assistance in the early days of the book; to the

Reverends Edward T. Douglas, S.J., Henry Sattler, C.S.S.R., and Walter Cavanaugh, C.S.S.R., for the many ways in which they do not realize they helped. The kindly insistence of Mother Mary Gemma, Superior General of the Missionary Sisters of St. Columban, who seemed to have a special sense of the need of this type of writing, is gratefully acknowledged.

The competence, forbearance, and genuinely friendly attitude of Mr. Eugene Prakapas made this task immeasurably easier. His understanding of the problems of a man who simultaneously was writing a book and trying to carry on the practice of obstetrics and gynecology was especially appreciated.

The hard work of typing and retyping this manuscript was done by my long-suffering secretary, Mrs. Anne Dowling, my former secretary, Mrs. Grace Hopkins Magazu, who managed to do her part while taking care of five children, and the Missionary Sisters of St. Columban who typed the final manuscript.

A word of gratitude must also be offered to those who, attending Pre-Cana Conferences or college lectures on marriage, have stimulated me by their questions to undertake this project. To all, I am most grateful.

My dad, Mr. Harry L. Lynch, Senior, made his usual contribution of matching his encouragement with enthusiasm. Finally, I am happy to acknowledge the help of my wife, Mary, whose wealth of patience, genuine interest, and seemingly limitless encouragement enhance my every effort.

W. A. L.

Dedicated

WITH ABIDING AFFECTION AND GRATITUDE

TO THOSE WHO HAVE SHOWN ME

THE GOOD LIFE,

THE ART OF SUCCESS IN MARRIAGE,

THE TRUE MEANING OF FAMILY LIVING,

AND

THE LOVE WHICH IS ESSENTIAL TO IT:

TO MY DAD

Harry Leo Lynch, SR.

AND MY LATE MOTHER

Mary Frances Lynch

TO MY MOTHER-IN-LAW

Mary Ellen Joyce

AND MY LATE FATHER-IN-LAW

Patrick Joseph Joyce

AND

to my own Mary

"Beloved sons and daughters, keep and care for with jealous solicitude the two-fold and holy inheritance left to you by our ancestors. The first is the Christian life of the family, Where it still survives, especially in the country, keep it and defend it.

"Yes, defend it, because even there it is in great danger of being lost.

"Where it has disappeared, especially in some workers' quarters in cities, rebuild it. You cannot give to your children and to your youth anything more precious than life and Christian perfection of family.

"The other inheritance is harmonious activity in public life. Without doubt, the aim of redemption is personal sanctification of all individuals. But according to God's plan of salvation, sanctification of individuals must be rooted and blossom and bear fruit in the community in which they live, which is itself vivified by faith in God and by the spirit of Christ. . . ."

Pope Pius XII

TO THE PEOPLE OF GERMANY, SEPTEMBER 4, 1949

DURUM: sed levius fit patientia quicquid corrigere est nefas—Horace, Ode XXIV
It is hard, but what may not be altered is made lighter by patience.

FOREWORD

In Christian theology, the local Bishop is the chief guardian of Faith and morality in the section of the Church he has been commissioned to serve. In our day, this task has been made considerably more difficult because traditional Christian concepts on the nature of marriage and marital morality are being assailed on every side. This breeds serious confusion in the minds of men who have been called to follow the Christian way of life and this cannot but be a mighty concern to the Shepherd whose task it is to lead them in their holy vocation.

The past few years have witnessed the publication of many books written to defend the Christian concept of marriage and marital love. Most of them, however, have been authored by priests. I am very pleased to write the foreword to this book on marriage written by a knowledgeable Catholic layman who is also an outstanding gynecologist and obstetrician.

For almost fifteen years Dr. William Lynch has been doing

an extraordinary service for the young people of this Archdiocese. He has given over three hundred Pre-Cana Conferences and is constantly in demand to lecture on marriage to Newman Clubs, Catholic colleges, and Catholic high schools. His frank discussions with young men and women on these occasions have led him to realize that there is a dearth of good material on Catholic marital morality comprehensible to the layman, that most Catholic colleges which do offer a course on marriage do not approach it from a realistic and mature point of view, and that many of our engaged couples have to resort to pseudo-scientific and hedonistic-oriented books on marital techniques because matters of this nature are often treated in a superficial manner by Catholic authors.

Dr. Lynch's *A Marriage Manual for Catholics* has been written as a result of the years of experience described above. It presents a reverent, practical, and realistic source of information about the physical, emotional, and esthetic aspects of marriage. In presenting this book to the Catholic public, the author has done a valuable service for the Bishops of our Church and has aided them considerably in making their arduous task a little bit lighter.

RICHARD CARDINAL CUSHING
Archbishop of Boston

CONTENTS

6. Premarital Examination and Conferences

7. The Marriage and the Honeymoon

8. The Facts of Love and Life

12. Miscarriage and Infertility

13. For Better or for Worse

EPILOGUE: Questions and Answers

A MARRIAGE MANUAL

FOR CATHOLICS

INTRODUCTION

The practice of marriage as an art, as a way of living, a stairway to happiness and heaven, is witnessed close at hand by very few people. I am privileged to be one of those. As an obstetrician-gynecologist, I see marriage born of love. I see love in all of its stages—early, joyful, maturing, painful, productive, God-fearing, and enduring. I see new life come into the world and all the joy that it brings with it. I see mothers face the birth process with courage and eager anticipation. I am also present at a birth the world consistently ignores—the birth of a mother. The obstetrician-gynecologist in a real sense helps a mother through her own swaddling clothes era, while the family and friends, seemingly heedless of her trials, settle down to monitor the baby's growth.

I see fathers emerge from parenthood shaken and proud, determined and fierce, gentle and loving.

I see families born; I see society grow.

From my daily work, I know love to be not a product of

1

the poet's mind but a providential gift preciously guarded by normal people and the most powerful force in human relations. No one can successfully fight it and no one can contain it because it grows by giving. Whoever mocks love outrages human nature, and those who embrace it within the context of Christian living reach home.

And so a physician, not a psychiatrist, a Catholic obstetrician-gynecologist rather than a clergyman, a lawyer, or a social worker, gathers his thoughts on marriage and living and offers them to the reader. The subjects discussed are suggested from recurrent questions posed at Pre-Cana Conferences, Newman Club discussions, lectures, and group discussions of marriage. The answers are inspired by daily observations of successful Catholic living and happy Catholic marriages.

From the nature of his calling, the physician must be concerned constantly with the individual, otherwise the patient-physician relationship is lost, and medicine becomes another mechanistic science. The physician feels that by the study of individuals, groups emerge from which he can learn something for the protection of the individual. By repeated contact with the individuals in happy marriages, he should be able to make some worthwhile observations for the protection and advice of other individuals in marriage. It may be somewhat daring for the physician to call himself a human scientist, but he should be just that. He should be sufficiently a scientist to be objective in his approach and make the facts prove themselves. But, above all, particularly with reference to marriage, he must never forget Terence's admonition, "Nothing that is human can be foreign to us."

The physicians who have had a unique and peculiar opportunity to view marriage have been the old-fashioned family doctors (who are encountered, unfortunately, less and less frequently in our American life) and the obstetrician-gynecologist. As a matter of fact, there are some who believe that the obstetrician-gynecologist is becoming in some degree the family doctor for the women of the nation.

The clergyman sees engaged couples before the wedding and may be called when marriages get into trouble. Not infrequently, the priest who writes or lectures on marriage is a hard-working member of a marriage court working with and trying to help desperate and often sick couples unhappy in their marriage. Ministers have frequently been inspired to embrace marriage counseling as a means of doing their part in stemming the divorce parade. The social scientists, whether they be sociologists or marriage counselors, usually study the interdependences among peoples in marriage, the personal inter-relationships involved in marriage, personal tragedies and their origins, and the impact of marriage and its difficulties upon society as a whole. They are equally concerned with customs, mores, and trends in the philosophy and thinking of the times which may affect marriage. Surveys and research occupy their time, and they are usually concerned with the study of the abnormal, the sick, and the variant. Surveys of the normal are difficult to find.

The prize-winning novelist writing about marriage usually treats man and woman in marriage at a rather heroic level, or at least talks about the so-called universal individual. The novelist of today is once again the instrument of realism, which too frequently is equated with the bizarre. The probate court judge, the lawyer, and the psychiatrist are primarily concerned with the pathology of marriage. They see the problems that lead to divorce and separation; they see the human wreckage, both adult and juvenile, that is found in the path of broken marriages; they see what is wrong with people who are trying to break the most sacred bond in their lives—and they attempt to discover the cause for such abnormal behavior. All of these groups see what is wrong in marriage and see what is wrong with people who enter into bad marriages. The individuals they see and study are ill—at least with regard to marriage. And so, they are very apt to speak from a survey of unhappy experiences, and from this background they attempt to distill information for the protection of the individual.

The modern obstetrician-gynecologist and the family doctor are privileged to help guide a mother through her nine months of pregnancy, in which she carries the fruit of the love of two people to its denouement in the delivery of the living child. We get the phone calls surreptitiously made by the "unworrying" father-to-be who actually shows a genuine concern for his growing family. We are privileged to see the father-to-be as something other than the comic-strip character so deftly portrayed in American life, and we know the genuine person who for so long now has been comic material—the American father. We also see people who have difficulties in marriage, but we see happy people, people in love, surmount these difficulties and see them draw closer together because of their problems. Most of the time it is our privilege, unique almost in medicine, to see people who are involved in happy marriages find the power of their love in their own lives and the meaning of the expression "count your blessings."

We speak, therefore, of the happiness we have observed in large numbers of people who have made happy marriages. We believe that the story of marriage, if it is to be completely told, must have certain scientific aspects. We believe further that evidence deduced from fair studies of married people as groups and within the community may be valuable and educative. However, we are sufficiently sentimental to believe that marriage, and particularly Christian marriage, is probably the most romantic story on earth. We believe that while you may be able to dissect marriage as an institution, it is very difficult to dissect it as a fact.

If marriage or romance has anything in the positive direction, it is mutuality, and even mutuality has its own dangers. "Togetherness" has become almost a status symbol or at least a concept of such fad-like proportions that the idea of marriage as a contractual institution has been lost in the pursuit of togetherness. And yet, the mutual natures of the partners rather than the differences need to be emphasized and explored.

This is somewhat difficult in the brittle culture in which we live. The individual has now become something that is defined rather than one who lives. Love is something that is opposed to hostility. Frigidity (horresco referens) instead of the affliction of a few has been given to us by Stekel as a consecrated phrase and has been repeated and stressed so often that the general public is under the impression that frigidity is a normal variant, which it most certainly is not.

Marriage has become a "contract of convenience," the Ten Commandments "rules of considerable value," and a person's word solemnly given is to be solemnly kept—as long as it is advantageous to all. This is the twentieth century we are told, with new freedoms, dimensions, and rights. Above all, we are told, we must be supremely "practical" in matters of marriage, children, children spacing, population, abortion, and morality. Once again we find springing up an adulation of science, scientific progress, new horizons, the conquests of man—forgetting that such adulation also includes the confusion that is the inevitable companion of progress.

Thus, one is not supposed to talk of marriage in these days unless one mentions eugenics and genetics, the proper breeding of man, artificial insemination, and the function of marriage in producing an intellectual aristocracy who will inevitably rule the world.

In the following pages, we hope to be human and humane. We plan to be practical about marriage, but also romantic;

biological, but a little bit spiritual, too; factual, but not coldly so; progressive, but not for its own sake, and please God, not in confusion. There is always a need for a hard look at all the facts of life. There is today perhaps an even greater need for an awareness of the great religio-philosophical verities, the great spiritual values, and the honest human sentiments of love, fidelity, and sacrifice.

1

The Meaning of

Marriage to a Catholic

Marriage is probably the most popular institution in the world, and it should be, because it leads to the happiness of more people consistently, generation after generation, than perhaps anything else. It is a temporal act performed by people with a real creative capacity, and since that creative capacity is fulfilled by cooperating with God, it has a spiritual nature as well. It presupposes deep human relationships and a solemn relationship with God of such a nature that it contains a note of infinity as well.

It is important, however, to remember that marriage is an institution. It is necessary that it be an institution for the good of the two people involved, for the perpetuation of the family, and for the proper rearing of children. Goethe said, "The sum which two married people owe to one another defies calculation. It is an infinite debt which can only be discharged through all eternity." Marriage raises the questions of incalculable debts and inestimable benefits of love fostered by millions of little things, and perhaps only in marriage can human beings really understand the true nature of the word thoughtfulness.

The Catholic concept of marriage raises certain primary issues of love, of perpetuation of children and family, and a relationship with God which binds the contract and which perhaps, in brief, may be put this way. We are all on our way back to God. The love of God is the reason for our existence and the cause for our redemption, and we are brought into this world as the fruit of the love of a man and a woman cooperating with each other and with God. It is man's nature to be created by love, to be born in love, to be reared in love, and to search unceasingly for love. It is man's nature to make the great circle from the love of God to the love of God.

In the world around us, people do one of two things—they either marry or they don't. Those who marry feel they can get closer to God, and more certainly and more effectively return to Him, by sharing their life and love in marriage. Those who choose the celibate life are convinced that it is easier to become a saint while single than while married. As St. Paul pointed out, "It is easier to be busy with the things of the Lord in the single state than in the married state."

And yet, even here, there is a type of marriage. There is the marriage of the individual to Christ and His Church in religious life. There is also the marriage of individuals to Christ's teachings while forgoing a marriage in the life of religion. Such lives are led by the distinguished, or not infrequently by the quiet, unheralded, Catholic laymen and laywomen who, remaining celibate, further Christ's Church by action and example.

Those who marry, therefore, elect, so to speak, a mutual assistance pact with another person whom they feel can aid them in getting back to God. It is no wonder then that

Catholics accept marriage as a serious thing. The selection of the person who is going to be your companion on your way back to God is a matter of great importance, and the selection must be carefully made.

Two people, then, enter into a marriage contract, which means they feel certain that their return to God will be easier, more certain, and more productive than it would be outside of marriage. It also means they undertake to bring other souls into the world in cooperation with God and to so rear and nourish them physically and spiritually that they too may find an avenue by which they may return to the Supreme Creator. Marriage, therefore, assumes transcendent importance, and the selection of the partner with whom to enter this contract becomes one of the most vital decisions in life.

In the marriage contract, each member gives himself to the other until death. More specifically, they give the rights to the reproductive or sexual functions to one another exclusively until death. Thus, the solidarity and integrity of the family is insured, the unity of their love is preserved, and the expression of their love made unique and personally flavorful.

Marriage, then, is a contract of love between two people until death. Since it is a contract (as it obviously is with two people agreeing to give rights to one another), justice demands that the contract be fulfilled. Since the contract is the one which introduces and forms the family and is a means of salvation, then obviously the contract must be fulfilled until death parts the couple. The good marriage, therefore, fulfills the virtue of justice. The poor marriage, crippled by the broken word, offends justice.

There are at least two other major virtues fulfilled in marriage. The consummate act of giving each other to one another in the most perfect way God has given them to express their love is in a real sense an act of charity. It is an act motivated by love of God and the desire to return to Him and by the love of a fellow man.

Chastity, which is so mocked by our ultra-sophisticated world today and misunderstood even by people who think of themselves as "scrupulous," is a very earthy virtue intended in a humane and delightful way for humans. It is the virtue of chastity which prevents love from becoming cheapened prior to marriage. And it is the virtue of chastity which, after marriage, nurtures and fulfills love in the home.

Chastity makes the act of love in marriage a meritorious act, an act pleasing to God and to humans. Chastity makes the breath of love sweet and its fruit healthy. It is the virtue of chastity which proves to the couple that their love can be strong enough to build a self-discipline before the marriage so that both are prepared to make whatever sacrifice may be necessary for the success of marriage. In short, the marriage act within the marriage state fulfills the virtue of chastity and is an act so meritorious to the marriage state that when performed in grace demands grace from God.

What Makes Marriage Holy?

Marriage is a contract entered into freely and solemnly before God and man. Its purposes are twofold. First, to produce and educate children, and second, to express, establish, and cement love in the conjugal act. As a couple enters into this contract, there is set up a new relationship with their God, with whom they will cooperate to bring forth children, and to whom and with whose help they may return together. It is this relationship with God Himself that makes the contract of marriage a contract that can be broken only by death.

It is this relationship that makes marriage not merely a contract but a sacrament. It makes marriage a holy thing. It is this real, living relationship with God Himself, bound by a contract solemnly given, which makes marriage so important to the Catholic and which is sometimes so difficult for the non-Catholic to understand. For this reason, some further explanation of the Catholic concept of marriage is in order.

God existed from all eternity. Since God is a Supreme Being and is All-knowing, He has a complete knowledge of His nature and, so to speak, a complete picture of Himself in His own mind, just as anyone can have a picture of himself in his own mind. We can look into a mirror and see what we look like and recognize what we see. We see a picture that moves, smiles, and acts just as we do. However, the life that we see in this image has no reality; the only reality is what is standing on one side of the mirror looking into it.

The difference between God and us in such a case is that the picture that God has of Himself in His own mind is alive and stands beside Him as the Second Person. Thus the Second Person is equal in every way with the Father. St. Paul says that the Son is ". . . the mirror of God's majesty and the splendor of His glory."

All of us have certain images that we try to convey by speech or writing, and to do this we use words. When God conveyed the picture that was in His mind of Himself He called that the Word of God. Thus Christ is called the Word of God. "In the beginning was the Word . . . and the Word was made flesh . . ." These two persons, God and the picture which God had of Himself in His mind, called the Word of God, existed as two distinct persons; both were God and equal in every way. The relationship that existed between them was that of Father to Son, not of brother to brother. As an idea is generated from our mind, so the Second Person of the Trinity came from the First Person in God by the process of generation, and They stand in Their relationship to one another as Son to Father and Father to Son.

The Father loves the Son with a real paternal love, and the Son returns the love to the Father with a filial love of devotion. Because both are God, they love each other with an infinite love. However because there cannot be two infinite loves in God, it is by the same infinite love that They love each other. This love personified and made a person is called the Holy Ghost.

The generation of the Son from the mind of the Father and the Holy Ghost proceeding from the love of both is something that is happening in every moment in God; it is an eternal act of God and is known as the Holiness of God. In the Trinity, therefore, the First and Second persons are, so to speak, taking the heart out of Their being and surrendering it to each other; and that heart is the Third person. This is what is described as the Home of God or the Divine Family of God Himself. Thus, the Trinity.

The marriage of human beings reflects the mystery of the Blessed Trinity itself, which illustrates the function married people are meant to perform in their efforts to get back to God. When God created Adam (the first person of the human trinity), He made him to His own image and likeness. When Eve (the second person of the human trinity) was created, she emerged from the first directly in the way that God has described for us. In the creation of the third person of the human trinity He put love into the hearts of Adam and Eve, and the fruit of that love was born as their first child. Thus, in the birth of every child is the completion of the human trinity which reflects the Blessed Trinity. The whole of God's plan in the creation of man is best summarized in the account given by God Himself in the Scriptures. When he had put life in the oceans of the earth, in the air, and in the forests He said, "Let us make man to Our own image." Let "us," the Three Persons, as it were, meeting in council, stress the image of the Trinity in this creation. "And God made man to His image. To the image of God He created him. Male and female He created them. And God blessed them saying: "Go, increase and multiply." Thus was the foundation of the human family—the first marriage, blessed in Heaven, modeled after the Divine family of God Himself.

It is easy to see, therefore, why marriage is a contract and why the relationship from that contract becomes such a holy thing in the sight of God and should be in the sight of man. It also is easy to see why the rights of marriage are to be preserved for that state and why when they are used outside of marriage they become an insult to God and to the image of the Trinity. As a matter of fact, God destroyed the whole world by the deluge because of such violations of the marriage contract. For the same reasons, He cut down Sodom and Gomorrah with fire and brimstone. For violating marriage and its contract, he struck Onan dead.

It is the Catholic belief that every sin against the purity of the contract of marriage, every attack against the marriage contract is in its essence an attack upon the image of the Holy Trinity. It is not only an attack on marriage itself but an attack on the Holy Family. It is a personal insult to God in the Blessed Trinity. If there is anything certain about the devil's existence, it is that he is opposed to the Blessed Trinity, the Home and Holiness of God. The devil cannot do anything to attack these directly and so he attacks the Trinity, the Home and Holiness of God, through its image on earth, the human trinity or marriage. It is not drafting incantations and witchery to say that the material and irreligious attitude of the present day towards marriage is an attack straight from hell. As a matter of fact, St. Paul says that our fight "is not against flesh and blood but against principalities and powers."

The Sacrament of Marriage

There are at least two other ways of looking at the Catholic concept of marriage. One is God's love of man. He died for love of man, to redeem him; and He instituted certain avenues of grace by which we may reach salvation. These avenues or sources of grace are known as the Seven Sacraments. These sacraments are offered or administered to people by certain selected men who are known as the ministers of the sacraments or the priests of God. God undoubtedly could have selected any number of ways in which these sacraments could have been administered. The fact is that he selected one specific way, the administration of His sacraments through His priests, who are given that power through one of the sacraments themselves, called Holy Orders. It is specifically and uniquely important, however, that there is one exception to this rule, and that exception is the sacrament of marriage.

The minister of a sacrament is a channel of grace to the soul to whom it administers that sacrament. In the sacrament of matrimony, the ministers of the sacrament are the individual partners in the marriage contract. They are, therefore, individual channels of grace one to the other in the sacrament of marriage. In a temporal sense, their first wedding gift to one another is the gift of each to the other; in a spiritual sense, their first wedding gift to each other is the grace of God. Thus is the life-stream of God Himself made to flow in the lives of people in marriage. This is why we say that one's partner in marriage is a means by which we return to God. This is why we say that God does not just join the partners in marriage; He is the link by which they are joined. For that reason no man can break the link. That is why no valid consummated marriage can be absolved or broken or annulled by any power on earth, including the Vicar of Christ, the successor to Peter, the Pope himself. And that is why Catholics hold strictly to the statement that what God hath put together let no man put asunder.

One final thought. In Christian thinking, the motif is always that Christ came on earth, died, and redeemed man in order that we might reach salvation. The focus is always on the coming of Christ and His works here on earth. This is as it should be; this was Christ's work and this is Christianity. However, it might be worthwhile for us to remember that while Christ as God is everywhere, in a certain sense, when Christ the God-man came on earth, He left Home, that is, He left the Family of the Blessed Trinity. When He came on earth, He was received with a coldness that has made the Inn of Bethlehem the symbol for lack of hospitality ever since. And He left the earth in the most vicious way that the mind of man could devise.

When we leave home, especially if we meet a cold reception in a new community, certain things will always remind us of home; we will turn to them with enthusiasm and with heartfelt feelings of joy. If we may dare to be just a little bit sentimental about our God, we may dare to think that there was perhaps one thing on earth that reminded God of His Trinity Home—and that was marriage, the human trinity of His creation. It is very significant that after thirty years of silence His first public appearance was at the marriage feast of Cana. It is even more significant that His first miracle was performed to save a bride embarrassment on her wedding day. The Catholic concept of marriage is that a couple, in preparing for their own salvation and honestly endeavoring to lead each other to salvation, should so lead their lives prior to marriage that they would be properly prepared to build within their marriage a home, a human trinity, so that Christ could call it home and visit there.

2

The Catholic Family

The time has come, we are told, for many things. We are advised to take a broad view of the space age, to prepare for the twenty-first century, to keep an eye on overpopulation, to study the continuing social evolution, to reappraise the role of religion, and to consider leaving to man more of the responsibility for himself.

Some social scientists would have us believe that the answer to our problems—from teenage delinquency to cold-war hostility—can be found at a purely ideological or political level or in a changed attitude of government towards its people and other governments. Others would have us believe that if we remain urbane, sophisticated, and wary the process of social evolution in its inexorable fashion will redefine or realign various social factors and eventually solve our common problems.

A priest in ancient Egypt some 3400 years ago is recorded as saying: "Youth is disintegrating. The youngsters of the land have a disrespect for their elders and a contempt for authority in every form. Vandalism is rife, and crime of all kinds is rampant among all young people. The nation is in peril." In the history of every nation there has been a prophet, priest, or philosopher who has warned that the road to destruction of a nation lies in the self-destructive habits of the young. And a lack of respect for authority has always been synonymous with the abdication by parents of their rights, privileges, and obligations.

The time, indeed, has come to consider many things. No nation is any better or more effective than its people. No nation can be led properly unless its people are honest, moral, and responsible. And no nation or its people can afford to stand still. Since continuing progress depends upon each new generation, the ultimate fate of any nation depends upon its young. So perhaps we should take a broad view of the space age—and even a closer look at the family. Family life and its success will determine the fruits of the twenty-first century. Population starts or stops within the family, and if, indeed, population control is necessary, it can only be properly initiated and effectively accomplished within the family circle itself. Perhaps there is a need for a reappraisal of the role of religion, but if so, it must be within the home, where any religion must be taught if it is to be vibrant and enduring. Broad and specific educational systems are necessary and even critically important, but they will function as well with their halls empty if the proper educative process has not been initiated in the home. The time, indeed, has come—for a defense of the family and a restatement and re-establishment of its necessary position.

Today the family labors under at least two burdens which make the proper discharge of family responsibility difficult. The fulfillment of sex as an appetite and an experience has become fashionable; sex has become biological instead of human, related to love in a sentimental and sometimes quasi-theatrical manner. But sex can only be equated with love within the family circle, and herein lies one of the greatest challenges to the family today.

Young people have been invited to experiment with sex, especially as a biological experience. Inevitably, pregnancy outside of marriage has been the result. These extramarital pregnancies illustrate the second great challenge to the family —the separation of reproduction from marriage. Marriage is separated from reproduction by contraception and a consideration of sex as an appetite. This same combination, in the hands of the immature and impatient young, leads to higher illegitimacy. Apart from any moral considerations, reproduction divorced from marriage is an irresponsible act and at the very least unfair *to the reproduced.*

There are three elements necessary to make a parent—a man, a woman, and God. The expression of the mutual love of all three leads to the formation of a family with the birth of a child. There should be no time in which people feel closer to God than at the birth of a child, and the birth of a family, when they have shared and, in a sense, imitated His generative properties. They grow and mature as individuals, as husband and wife, as lovers, and they become blessed children of God and special giants to their own children. When they are willing and anxious to build a good family based upon their love for their children and their children's love for them, they become, indeed, the handmaid and servant of the Lord and teachers of filial devotion.

The Role of the Wife and Mother

The wife and mother must first of all recognize and enjoy the privilege of being a woman. She must be aware of the differences between her and her male partner and enjoy these differences. She must be proud of the purpose for which she was born, of the bodily functions and emotions which make her a woman, and proud that she is happy in doing womanly things. It has been said that the happiest women, like the happiest nations, have no history. This is undoubtedly true, particularly inasmuch as it refers to a woman's preoccupation as a woman with things that are personal, that involve people as individuals, that involve the growing mind and the growing body. Her accomplishment is in producing the new generation; her greatest accomplishment is in producing a generation that is better than hers, one that can more swiftly, safely, and surely return to God. She writes her history in the minds of children, and if she is a real woman, she guides and nourishes carefully, softly, and gently, the courage and ambition with which future history can be written.

As a woman she sees the little things in people. She is the font of charity in the home, the source of the second and third chance. She is the one who shows by example and teaching that love is an all-embracing force that involves God, husband, children, country, and community in very wonderful if very different ways. She points out to small children that love always finds room for mercy when justice must be served. She is the preserver of the sense of humor and clearly demonstrates, diplomatically and without affront to anyone's pride, how a little humor can relieve the tension of a difficult moment.

The wife and mother, handmaid of the Lord, is the great humanitarian. Her life has to be the Golden Rule and her attitude subjective. She makes sweet uses of humility and teaches even a small boy that sentimentality can be masculine. She was probably the first one in history to throw away a book. So effective a weapon has this practice become that it has now become almost a sign of genius, at least in certain circumstances, to know when to "throw the book away."

The Christian wife and mother has been called a slave to her husband, her children, her home, her community, her country, and her God. The wife and mother works hard, often to a degree for which she is not given the proper credit; her hours are long and unpredictable. Using the term slave, however, misses much of the meaning of living and almost all of the meaning of love. To serve one's spouse, children, community, country, and God is the definition of the solid citizen. It is true that this defines the citizen's function according to Christian thinking, but I think few would doubt that the woman in the family, the mother of the family, in her own quiet way, in the confines of her home, is the solid citizen of our nation. The married woman's rewards, like the man's, are essentially to be found in the satisfaction of a deed well-done. But, because of his dual role outside and inside the home, the man also gets adulation and reward from the community; the woman receives much of her inner satisfactions and rewards in love.

> "Shall she come down and on our level stand?
> Nay, heaven forbid it! May a mother's eyes,
> Love's earliest home, the heaven of babyland
> Forever bend above us as we rise."—J. B. Tabb

Whose eyes have been the earliest home of love has no need of history.

The Role of the Husband and Father

The first requisite of a husband and father is that he be secure in the knowledge of the privilege that is his in being a husband and father. When writing or speaking in praise of mothers and motherhood, an author usually mentions the fact that so little has been written about fathers—except in humor, of course. The implication is that there is little or nothing stimulating or inspiring about the concept of fatherhood. This is not surprising. Along with the attempts to downgrade the family by separating marriage and reproduction, love and sex, is a concomitant effort to "liberate" the mother (from the family, that is) and to tear down a valid picture of the father as the head of the house. A materialistic view of life cannot tolerate competition between the family and the state.

It was not always so. In the old days the family was important; family ties were strong and family pride actually was an exercise in the love of God. The literature of the ancient world is replete with the position of respect which was afforded the father and which indeed, is retained in some (too few) of the so-called "old" countries of the world today. The literature portrays the strong, honorable masculine figure who is simultaneously a loyal son motivated by real filial devotion and a gentle, loving father. The ancient Romans, possibly taking the lead from Virgil's hero, held a good husband and father to be of more value than the best senator of the republic. And in one ancient Book that is ever new, the Gospel of Jesus Christ, the father is constantly portrayed as a beloved figure. Jesus constantly talks about His Father and describes fathers in general in His parables as people who are interested, protective, concerned, and loving toward their children. He doesn't hesitate to castigate men who have done wrong, but the father, in relation to his children, is always gently portrayed. And in the parable of the Prodigal Son, He offers to all fathers an example and advice.

The father has a different voice and a different tone of voice than the mother; his attitude, manner, and actions are meant to be firm, comforting, and directive—and disciplinary when needed. The father must be concerned with any action contemplated by or affecting the family or any of the children. He must establish an order and a sense of order that by example and teaching will emphasize to the children the importance of the who, what, where, when, and how. To protect order, there must be discipline. The discipline must be meted out with justice so that the child finds security in the discipline of one who cares enough to correct, honorably, morally, and politely. Justice must be taught to children even at the expense of a moment's discomfort for them. The husband and father must be the administrator. It is his distasteful task to look at a situation objectively while his wife deals with it in personal terms. A child must learn from his father that a word given or an agreement made is a contract binding in justice, and that a precious thing called honor, on the possession of which all men are judged, requires that the word be kept and the contract fulfilled. But the father is required to go further; should the word not be kept and the contract not fulfilled, then the price must be paid, and discipline must be used to teach the child this important truth and give him a feeling of security that someone is watching out for his honor.

The father is intensely interested in earning the respect of his child. Whether his work is such that honors come easily, or whether he considers himself an ordinary man with an ordinary job which he does well, all fathers want the admiration of their children for being what they are—men and fathers. Pride tastes sweeter to the male than it does to the female, and the pride which a father has for his family and which it has for him is one of his richest rewards.

There is a source of envy in family relations. The mother's constant association with the child—especially through the preschool years—gives her an intimate knowledge and a close, if somewhat naturally prejudiced, appraisal of her children.

In a kindly or nostalgic way, the average father envies his wife to some extent, because his job denies him any extended period of time with his children. But this is one of the sacrifices that must be made to the modern world.

It has been said that the father is also a slave to his wife, his children, his home, his community, his country, and God; again, we deny the validity of the term slave, unless it be modified by "willing," and we point to these traits as the definition of the solid citizen.

The Parents as Educators

Education within the home involves a slow, gradual, and progressive training of the children to a philosophy of life. It is an education to a sense of time and place, person and propriety; to the place of authority and obedience, to a proper understanding of charity, and to respect for the reasonable and prudent man with thoughtful consideration of family and neighbors in all decisions; to the knowledge that each child is a human creature, a member of society, with rights and obligations. It is an education to induce filial devotion, so that children will do things and do them properly out of love for their parents, just as their parents do things properly out of love for their children.

Education in the home indelibly establishes in the child's mind a sense of loyalty to family and an understanding of the obligation that good families owe to the community. The properly educated child understands that there is a better society in his home than outside, that there is more security in the home—based on fairness and discipline—than outside the home, and that there are better answers to his questions in the home. He learns that the home offers better stimuli to progress and ambition, that there is more assistance and understanding there, and that as educators his parents are fair. Children react violently to injustice. A child will forgive a teacher almost any degree of incompetence provided that teacher is fair. On the other hand, it will accept no prodigious accumulation of knowledge if the teacher is unfair. So, if the parents are to function as parents, to induce filial devotion, to encourage ambition, and to educate properly—they must be fair. Their function is not to correct the unfairness that other people have shown to one or more of their children; their proper function is to show, by their example and their insistence, that fairness applies to each member of the family.

Any parent of experience and all teachers know that the great educational drive is made at home. Parents cannot abdicate their educational function. There are some burdens the school cannot assume, some tasks the school cannot accomplish; both the school and the parent, as well as the child, realize this. This brings us naturally to that field of education which is properly the parent's function, which the school, in any case, is reluctant to undertake, and about which doctors are always asked—sex education of children.

If we agree that the primary educational function rests with the parents and if, as educators, the parents must be fair, and if they are involved and interested in the supreme care of their child educationally as well as physically, morally, and emotionally—then however awkward or embarrassing the question on sex, the parent should not shrink from giving some kind of answer to it. The simplest method is the earliest method. When the child first asks the so-called embarrassing question about the meaning and significance of his or her genitals or the origin of babies, then the answer, commensurate with his age, should be direct, immediate, and above all, simple. Children are not interested in doctoral dissertations on where babies come from. The attitude of children to all subjects is direct and simple. Their questions are direct and simple, and they expect only direct and simple answers. *The importance of the answer rests not in its completeness, but in its calculated effect to keep the child coming back to the parent for subsequent answers.*

It has been estimated by those who have studied the problem that the average child has some knowledge of sex, however incomplete or erroneous, by the age of eight. So if the questions start at age four, the parents should recognize that they will continue through and beyond the age of eight, whether they are directed to the parents or someone else. This means, fundamentally, the parents must decide whether they want their child to gain such information in controlled stages or in a hit-or-miss, right-or-wrong fashion from other children, younger or older, or other adults. It is essentially a question of whether the parents want their child to get the right or the wrong attitude towards sex, to get information or misinformation. It is an opportunity for the parents to explain that sex is something beautiful, not bad, loving, not animalistic; and that it was fundamentally God's idea in the first place and therefore good for both the parent and the child to know.

No one can tell a parent how to answer his own child. Parents and their children develop a language which is peculiar to themselves. But when a parent and child do not meet on the subject of sex, or any other subject, it means, fundamentally, on one subject at least they are strangers, on one subject there is a barrier or a fear between them. I believe it was Schiller who said, "A mother's lap is an island from which fear cannot get the child." Much of the sex education of the child rests with the mother. This is not a pre-conceived plan on anybody's part except that of Providence. Most original questions on sex are addressed to the mother because the child lives with her twenty-four hours a day during the preschool period. So, women must understand that if they want their child coming back to them for information, this is one subject which they must not dodge (although occasionally a mother may refer an older child to the father).

All questions should be met with gentleness, frankness, and responsibility. I frequently talk to groups of high school students—indeed, sometimes to entire high school student bodies—and I am always impressed by the seriousness and sincerity with which even high school freshmen address themselves to the problem of sex—and by what seems to be a real need for information. Unfortunately, parents are avoiding their responsibility on this particular subject. In the last twenty years, illegitimacy has increased 150 per cent, more than half of which is credited to teenagers. Venereal disease is increasing at an almost unprecedented rate with between one and two million cases of syphilis alone reported in this country every year. When one comes face to face with the fact that half of the people attending public venereal disease clinics are children, one begins to understand how serious the problem is and how necessary it is for children to get the proper education about sex: to learn that chastity is a virtue; to learn that sex is the natural expression of love for purposes of reproduction and that its fulfillment is to be found with the beloved in marriage. These are the concepts that must come from the parents—and only the parents can teach them. The child who is brought up in a properly oriented family and who can see how powerful is the working of love in the family will grow up with the proper attitude towards sex. Illegitimacy, venereal disease, promiscuity, and homosexuality are on the increase, and their flourishing indicates not only the presence of disease but a lack of respect for other people, for themselves, and for morality. The younger generation is so involved in rebellion against all authorities, celestial and otherwise.

When marriage is properly contracted by people in love, to produce a family according to God's plan and live within the privilege of man and woman, the husband and wife, father and mother, become properly the means of salvation for one another and sources of grace for their children. As educators the parents are obliged to do whatever is necessary for the care of their children. Sex was God's idea in the first place; only people make it dirty—parents can make it beautiful.

To paraphrase a well known saying, if instead of a gem or even a flower, one can cast the gift of a lovely thought into the mind of a child, one is giving as parents should give.

Family Living

Even successful marriages involve quarreling. Two people with backgrounds which are different to some degree are bound to have some conflicting ideas, sometimes on minor subjects. Discussion of these ideas at the wrong time or in the presence of irritating elements can lead to a quarrel. Quarrels, like everything else, can be good or bad. The good quarrel is healthy if it allows both partners to let off steam— but it is good because the problem is the issue and the quarrel is simply a slightly more painful way of finding the solution to the problem. A quarrel is bad or destructive when the issue becomes lost in what the Romans used to call an "ad hominem" argument—when *the person* defending an issue or a problem is abused and the issue is largely ignored.

Even in quarreling, the parent is the teacher. The child is a steady even an avid learner in the home school. Children quarrel as readily as they eat. If the quarrels they observe are constructive, productive, amicable, adult, and not abusive, then they have been exposed to a good model and the creeping state of adulthood has drawn closer.

Parents might remember that if they must quarrel, if they keep in mind that young ears are listening, they will quarrel productively and reach fruitful conclusions.

An understanding, companionable, and loving wife and mother oriented to her husband, her home, and her children is one of God's noblest creatures. To reach this exalted state she needs the blessing of God, the highest personal motivation, and the love of a good man. To maintain this position she must acquire early an ability to put first things first. The best wives and mothers do not always have a house in spotless order. A properly oriented husband will realize this and appreciate that the mother of his children is more concerned with the personal values in her life than with the perfection of her housework.

Thus is the home made, and made largely by the wife and mother. When the home is built on understanding, companionship, and the proper evaluation of personal values, it becomes a place for comfortable living and a haven for a harassed and tense husband, who can drop his work at its door and enter into the comfort and solace of an atmosphere created by his companion in life.

Perhaps George Eliot put it best: "I should like to know what is the proper function of women if it is not to make reasons for husbands to stay at home and still stronger reasons for bachelors to go out."

When a father returns home, his wife and family expect him to be tired but interested, tense but comforting, worried yet offering security. His resources are frequently limited, but his plans and ambitions fill his thoughts. He soon learns to think less of his future and more of theirs. His contacts with his own children and society are frequently limited, so

many fathers settle for a chance to offer their children opportunities and to teach them justice—sometimes a justice
they themselves have never known. The wise wife will
recognize that such a retreat does not represent defeatism
but rather a retrenching operation to allow him the satisfaction of doing well those things he can do (for his family).
The happiest women have no history; most fathers have to
ignore it. They both have to *make* it in their children.

A child is nature's fairest fashioned and one of God's
choicest rewards. He carries with him interest and curiosity,
a directness of approach, and such a guileless inquiry that
you are compelled to look into the world he opens—and you
are rewarded. A child invites new definitions of trust and
security. No one confers upon you more dignity, or honor;
no one offers more love and laughter. A child uncovers a soft-
ness and sentimentalism you never knew you had, and its
hand in your hand makes you feel the giant it knows you
to be.

A child puts the capital letter in Family, dots the "i" and
curves the "y." He asks that you love him enough to make
him self-reliant. He wants to be knowledgeable, God fearing,
courageous, and daring. He wants to know the right. He
wants an easy conscience and sweet sleep. All these are his
for the asking—in the family. These are the precious gifts of
parents.

3

The Selection of a Partner

The idea of marriage as an interesting way of life may occur to a girl as early as the age of twelve; usually it will not occur to a boy before his late teens. But at whatever age it occurs, the selection of a partner with whom you propose to travel the road back to God is of paramount importance. The task of evaluating an individual's past, background, and origins, and from this knowledge projecting into the future what his or her reactions are apt to be under certain circumstances, appears to require the wisdom of Solomon. The fact is that no such Solomonic wisdom is necessary. What *is* required is a serious view of marriage and a serious attempt well within the confines of romance to estimate a future partner. This doesn't mean there is only one individual in the entire world for you. On the other hand, neither does it mean that you look for a type of individual. Somewhere in between, among people you know and meet, there must be at least one person whose seriousness of purpose matches yours, and whose ideas of a life companion seem akin to yours.

One of the most refreshing things I encounter in dealing with people who are happily married and producing families, and who at thirty, thirty-five, or forty are still so obviously in love, is their repeated comment when drawn out on the subject that their mutual attraction was a rather sudden thing and that they have been perpetually amazed and grateful for the way in which their desires, their likes and dislikes, and their actions, instinctive and intuitive, have dovetailed and molded together.

I hold no brief for or against love at first sight. The more experience I have in such situations, the more I am convinced that in many instances love does occur at first sight, but it is not recognized as such. And the more solemnly and more powerfully grows my conviction that the old and simple statement—recently castigated as sentimental nonsense—that marriages are made in heaven may not be too short of the mark.

Marriage was meant to be bathed in romance and to be born of romance. Things loving and sentimental were meant to surround marriage. This is as it should be because people are sentimental, and they tend to be loving. But we have said repeatedly that marriage is also an important personal and permanent institution which people with a serious purpose elect as a perpetual state. Let those who object to dissecting or analyzing their future mate take a careful look around them in their own community and study the flow of data coming from the divorce mills; they will see the results of haphazard choice.

It must never be forgotten when contemplating marriage that the mate you choose is going to have intimate and prolonged contact with you, your children, and your property. This may sound like a dissection of your life; it is not.

It pinpoints the intimate contact which your mate is going to have with the three most important things in your life. And, of course, a Catholic must add a fourth, for your mate is going to be intimately involved with your attempt at reaching God.

Marriage has been glamorized by advertising media. The public, on the basis of material that is fed into the news media, is led to believe that this or that prominent couple in the entertainment or social world are ideally matched. Obviously, such judgments are dangerous at best. The difficulty, however, is that they are contagious. We constantly see the immature mind, the undisciplined mind, and the emotionally motivated personality leaping into a contract of marriage on the basis of a physical or even a sexual attractiveness. This is the sophisticated rule of the day.

The primary attraction between two people for marriage, whether it is conscious in them or not, is a psychological one. People marry personalities. People marry individuals that have been molded for a period of twenty or more years into a definite personality with certain backgrounds, habits, and reactions. This composite personality enters into a personal relationship in marriage which will last for better or for worse, for richer or for poorer, in sickness and in health, until death.

One does not dissect, to use a controversial word, the personality readily or easily; nor is it always possible for one to classify all of the features that make up the personality of an individual or which make that personality attractive. It is important, however, to make some sort of an attempt; the happiness of too many people depends upon it. It is tragic to see a girl catapulted into marriage by a crush on the local athlete, or a man captivated by 34-24-34 measurements.

Evaluating Your Prospective Mate's Personality

One of the first things people do when they meet and have their first few dates is subconsciously judge their relationship to one another. This is a complex problem even for the trained mind, but there is a relatively simple way of approaching it.

Where the interest is purely biological, at an animalistic level, either member of the partnership or both mutually look to see what can be done *to* the other person. This has been called the wolf approach, but it is closer perhaps to the canine. Such a relationship has been proven to be a poor one even for the proper breeding of dogs and has, therefore, no place in a relationship between people.

The diffident June lover and the tyro in romance who is somewhat inept and uneasy or who finds in someone a vague, pleasant personality trait which is attractive, spends much time wondering, planning, and plotting what can be done *with* her or him. This is still an attempt to attract, to please. This is puppy love in its first phases, and for the immature individual this liaison or any number of liaisons will never reach beyond this point.

On the other hand, there is no question about the attitude of the person genuinely in love. He or she is satisfied with another's personality and is enchanted by the possibilities of further exploring their mutual likes, interests, and satisfactions. It begins as a delightful minor obsession and, as the course of love proceeds, becomes a major one. For the person in love is constantly preoccupied with the question of what can be done *for* her or him. This reaction bespeaks a maturity, a general philosophy of life, a depth of feeling, a sincerity of purpose which will be obvious to the person beloved; it is the giver going with the gift, the true expression of thoughtfulness and consideration.

The personality traits which make a good marriage are the same traits which are found in a good person who enjoys living and who is in turn enjoyed by other people.

The first is *honesty*, intellectual and otherwise. An old proverb states you can shut the door on a thief but not on a liar, and I think this is never so cruelly true as in marriage. A lack of honesty seriously undermines a person's chances of success with other people. A lack of honesty between partners in marriage undermines the contract itself, since the day soon comes when all statements, including the statement made on the day of the wedding, fall under the shadow of doubt.

The example of dishonesty to children by a parent represents a horrible and peculiar brand of scandal which cries to heaven for vengeance. And a lack of honesty regarding property undermines material security, which in a marriage afflicted by dishonesty is usually the first to go or the only thing left.

Attitudes towards other people are important because they are usually consistent. An individual who is pleasant, charming, gracious, and considerate to the fiancé and grudging, grumbling, worrisome, petulant, or unreasonable to other people may be legitimately suspected of being a superb actor for the benefit of the fiancé. You don't live only with one another in marriage. It is true that you live with one another more closely than anyone else, but you also live with children who make demands upon your time, effort, and energies; with property, investments, bills, debts, and other obligations; and with in-laws, friends, and relatives. If it is true that no man is an island unto himself, it must be abundantly clear that a family is a community, and the person you marry must be capable of living in that community.

Much has been written, read, preached, and sung about the vain attempt of one individual to change another *after* marriage. What happens is that a person sees in a prospective mate a different attitude towards persons, places, or things, an attitude either unusual, abnormal, or something thoroughly distasteful. Instead of reading this as a danger signal, the person persists in marrying, hoping that time will bring reforms and forgetting that he or she is marrying a personality whose habits, customs, weaknesses, and strengths have been molded and fortified for twenty-odd years, and that there is little likelihood that another twenty years will change them *materially*.

A person must have enough maturity to make a serious effort. This is, I know, a rather trite phrase to summarize a personality trait necessary in a good marriage. It might instead be called "the will to win." Because marriage is a serious business, a serious effort is required. And that effort must be made in perspective. No one, for example, would be happy married to a "scrup" (one who is inordinately worried about all of the moral implications of every act within marriage). And it is difficult for marriage to be successful when one spouse is either a spendthrift, miser, glutton, or alcoholic. But to be successful, you must be capable of striking out, making decisions after due consideration, and following through on your decisions.

A healthy optimism is needed for a good marriage partner. Look for a partner who wants to keep things simple and let the good things happen. The pessimist is seldom happy even when he is convinced he is a realist, and he breeds only worry. The incurable optimist is apt to be emotionally motivated in judgments; the healthy optimist takes stock of the situation and implements a calculated judgment with confidence and courage.

A marriage partner must have the ability to give and take.

In the language of marriage, this is generally spoken of as the ability to make effective compromises. Two individuals will inevitably disagree in certain situations. If they are sufficiently serious and reasonable, they will appreciate diversity of opinion; and they will understand when one course is neither clearly more correct nor more desirable than the other and agreeably compromise.

A person must be able to make mental adjustments. One of the great "discoveries" of the twentieth century has been the fact that people make mental "adjustments." Modern psychiatry, in its dissection of human emotions, tends to give formal names to processes which people have been experiencing for centuries. The idea is to try to avoid marrying someone with a neurosis—a term which has been so misused that a further word of explanation seems in order. Most doctors, I believe, feel that most people are neurotic in their behavior at least once every day if they are normal, so to try to find the one person who is not neurotic in any of his or her activities is probably tantamount to seeking the king of Utopia. The whole problem of mental adjustment really comes down to the attitudes that people have towards life, living, and their particular situation. Most people, I think, would be deterred from entering into a liaison with an individual who decides he or she is not going to like a particular area, person, or situation before they have had a chance to experience it. In other words, we seek someone who will try to adjust to a situation which cannot be immediately improved. The self-centered, egotistical, therefore neurotic, individual is more apt to be lonely, moody, or easily hurt. The give and take of marriage creates sufficient strains at times to tax the healthiest of people adequately supported by genuine love. If one or both of the partners cannot adjust mentally in a difficult situation, then the strain on the family is increased that much more.

Consideration is important. Consideration for spouse, for children, and for other people is a basic trait of a healthy individual who has some consideration for his God and fellow man. And anyone who daily tries to make another person's day a little bit easier finds his own day becomes a great deal easier.

There should be self-confidence. As in all the cases discussed above, we look for the moderate man. The egotistical, over-confident individual is apt to be neurotic and collapse in the presence of immediate adversity. The person who lacks self-confidence to the point of constantly requiring a crutch to bolster his or her ego can be a burden in marriage. The person who has a quiet self-confidence is the mature individual who knows what he wants. Furthermore, he or she is living in the conditions and with the person he wants most, and his self-confidence is something that has been built up by having made careful and correct decisions in the important things in life.

Kipling, in his poem, "If," describes a mature individual who has acquired faith in himself and knows that the happiness he has is worth fighting for, and that if he only will continue to fight for it despite all adversities, he will be able to retain it. The person who even to the end, after seeing his or her life broken, can stop and rebuild it with worn-out tools, should be able to meet any challenge in marriage and family life.

Above all in the selection of a partner, you should look for a person who is mostly concerned with your happiness. This person should realize that your happiness involves spiritual as well as physical things; he or she needs to be warm, honest, and stable, and his or her definition of love should be the same as yours. There must be some reciprocity of feeling so that one may complement the other in the production of a family. The only true status symbols in marriage are a healthy love and a happy family.

Disparities in Age, Education, Background

The social considerations of marriage entail a person's ability to accept and exercise responsibility. If a person cannot do this in marriage, it is exceedingly doubtful that he or she can succeed in any phase of living. The responsibilities of marriage normally involve the health and salvation of each partner, the security of the home, the security of the children, the education of the children, and their proper development. A responsible or, if you like, a mature person is mindful of the past, working hard at the present, and has a definite plan for the future.

Age and maturity generally are placed together. This is unfortunate, for they do not necessarily coincide. Age and maturity may go along together, as in the person who grows old gracefully, but many young people are more mature than their elders. Age is inevitable, maturity is not; it eludes some people completely.

The question is often asked how a couple's disparity in age may affect their marriage. Many factors are involved here, but I think we can roughly approximate the relationship of age to successful marriage. If the man is equal in age or slightly older than his bride, from the point of view of age, the marriage generally works out very well. If the woman is slightly older than the groom, but only slightly, ordinarily there is no difficulty. The older a couple are, particularly in the forty- to fifty-year age group, the less a disparity of age affects their happiness and success. In other words, a marriage between a sixty- and a forty-year-old person would not be likely to generate appreciable difficulties, whereas a twenty-year span between the ages where one member was only twenty could spell considerable trouble. The problem, if there is one, so far as age is concerned, is found in the marriage of the young person and the one who is ten or more years older than he or she.

Song writers, poets, and novelists wax sentimental over May-and-December weddings. In actual life, they often present real problems. Where there is a great difference in age in a marriage, the younger one of the two partners is almost always the woman. It is rare, even peculiar, for a young man to enter into a marriage with a considerably older woman. Marriages between older men and younger women (a twenty-year difference) have been successful, but there are obvious handicaps. A twenty-year or even a ten-year difference in age between individuals can make considerable difference in their attitude towards the number of children in the family, their discipline, their future, and their education. For instance, the attitude of a sixty-year-old and a forty-year-old parent towards a twenty-year-old young adult can be as different as the gulf between generations is wide. The interpretation of what is liberal and conservative varies greatly in people of a twenty-year age difference. In an extra twenty years one may run into a frightening experience which materially colors his or her vision. Social and sexual drives of people twenty and forty years of age can vary tremendously. A ten-year age difference apparently is much less significant, but the consensus of opinion is that marriage partners should not differ in age more than five years, if possible.

Another problem often encountered in marriage is the discrepancy between the educational levels of the partners. Unfortunately, an educational disparity in marriage often creates dangerous ramifications which are seldom publicized. For example, if a wife is better educated than her husband, she probably will be more intellectual than the wives of his friends, and they will be prone to accuse her of snobbishness. This makes social contact between these families difficult. A woman with a highly disciplined mind, unless she has been trained to value her womanliness, is in danger of becoming domineering, forward, and even arrogant. Under these circumstances, educated women are reluctant to enter into a relationship with a man whose educational level is considerably below theirs, not merely for the obvious reason that they would have difficulty finding things to discuss, but because women instinctively realize that you can tread on almost any phase of a man's personality except his pride.

A person who has been trained in logic, who has a disciplined mind, who either knows the answers or knows where to find them, is apt to be much more direct, intellectual, and less emotional than one who has not had a formal education. There are exceptions, heroic individuals with native intelligence who have been able to educate and discipline themselves. But usually a disparity in education in marriage creates a problem of communication—the couple find it difficult to talk things out, which is the necessary prelude to effective compromise.

It is perhaps significant that when such a marriage does succeed, the man is usually more educated than the woman. What accounts for the greater success? The explanations are perhaps as many and varied as there are marriage counselors and people. Generally, I think, the woman can make sweeter uses of humility than can the man; in such a situation she can use her peculiarly womanly talents to support and inspire her husband. Furthermore, women in our society are rarely drawn into intellectual discussions; they are more active in their roles as wives and mothers—and they are judged more on these bases. Finally, when in social circles of a lower educational level (and this sounds terribly snobbish), the educated male is apt to be much more accepted and respected than the female would be in the same situation, as we have already pointed out. This double standard is in no way justified, but such is the way of people.

Education in itself cannot hurt a marriage; on the contrary, it should help considerably in solving some of its inevitable problems. The mental discipline found in education should help to keep the pattern of discussions and decisions within a logical path. And even a superficial study of the social sciences and history and literature should bring a better understanding of life and the world.

As might be expected, the divorce rate is proportionately lower among college graduates than among graduates of secondary or grammar schools. Even when the marriage fails, evidence indicates that the college graduate endures a bad situation longer for the sake of the children. However, there is reason to believe that divorce in college students is on the upswing, possibly as a result of recent ultra-liberal thinking and preaching for freedom of sex. If such attitudes prevail, we are in danger of inbreeding irresponsibility into marriage rather than bringing responsibility and maturity through education.

If the important aspects of what to seek in a marriage partner were to be summarized under one general heading, it would be a "philosophy of life." This does not mean that a person looks for someone who has a knowledge of Santayana, Dewey, or Aristotle; a philosophy of life concerns a person's thinking about religion, children, family, responsibility of parents, wealth, social position, and money. All of these things are important, but when you are looking for someone to marry, they become critical. These ideas should be consciously raised, discussed, and evaluated prior to marriage. A dichotomy in two persons' philosophy of life usually results in the partners being cut off from one another on this particular item. These are the problems that cause the most serious arguments and produce the most lasting wounds. Indeed, it is not improbable that important differences on at least two of the items comprising a philosophy of life could make a successful and enduring marriage almost impossible.

One of the most important of these items is religion. More will be said about religion when the discussion turns to mixed marriages, but essentially if marriage is the means which two people have to guide them back to God, it becomes automatically difficult for such a couple to achieve that end if their religious beliefs are sincere and are different. A sincere religious belief is so personal that no compromise is possible, and upon this all-important subject, such a couple remain strangers.

The number of children and their spacing in a marriage is a consideration, the importance of which is usually affected by circumstances after marriage. It is important, of course, because it intimately affects a couple as individuals and as husband and wife; but it is difficult to come to any hard and fast agreement on numbers before marriage. Even where the couple's religious beliefs are the same their ideas regarding a desirable number of children may be diametrically opposed. One partner may have been brought up to believe that all children in excess of three are a social nuisance or that having three children in four years is something akin to irresponsible morality. This may result in the charge that he or she doesn't understand the meaning of the vocation of marriage and the countercharge that he or she married for play. It is difficult to see how people genuinely in love could enter into marriage without coming to a broad agreement on such questions. The resolution of such opposite opinions is extremely difficult and extremely traumatic when occurring after marriage, unless the couple has a proper understanding of the dignity and responsibilities of family life.

Similarly, within broad limits, whatever is important to a couple should be decided before marriage. Is family life to compete with social life? Is the bill for the baby sitter to be equated with the bill for food? Is marriage, indeed, to be equated with the family? Will the parents be available as much as possible for the education and discipline of their children? Which holds primacy—the development of a family or development of the parent as an individual? I think all parents must be made to realize that the family comes first and that individual independence must be sacrificed to some extent for the sake of the family.

Money or the lack of it assumes a large role in people's lives. To what extent it affects the life of a prospective marriage partner should be determined before the ceremony. The financial compromises which are sometimes necessary in marriage will be difficult to make if one partner craves money (and the social position that goes with it). Persons who are convinced that money, wealth, and social position can buy happiness for themselves and their children, are a grave risk in marriage; these are grounds for even considering breaking off the engagement. Young people approaching marriage with such ideas generally have been feeling such convictions for some time and are not easily dissuaded from them, even under the conditions of family living. In such situations, a compromise, if possible at all, frequently leaves in its wake frustration and bitterness. Much unhappiness can be avoided if the subject is explored prior to marriage. Perhaps, indeed, some marriages doomed to failure could be avoided if this subject were properly discussed.

A person's hobbies in marriage at least should not be distasteful to his or her partner. It's ideal when two people are found in marriage who are enthralled with golf or stamp collecting, but this does not usually happen. When a hobby is time-consuming (such as golf), the hobbyist should be considerate of his or her partner and be willing to make some compromises. If a hobby is pursued in a fair and reasonable way it is entirely possible that eventually the spouse may be attracted to it or at least can become proud of the ability of his or her partner. No hobby can ever be permitted to interfere in any unfair way with the marriage relationship or family consideration.

The breadwinner's work is not as a rule subject to extensive discussion, particularly if it is profitable, steady, and pleasant. Most women have sufficiently practical minds to realize this. Even if a woman has an intense dislike for her husband's occupation, as a practical aspect of living, she soon learns to live with it. If, on the other hand, the work is of an interim type or a stepping stone to something better, it is not at all illogical for the couple to talk over their future plans. However, in the final analysis, unless there is some major change in geographical location, which is particularly difficult and irksome to the wife and family, the decision should be within the province of the husband. If the husband's work should become so distasteful that it becomes a subject to be avoided, then volunteer or community work, which is pleasant for both partners and which can be done by both in their spare time, should be fostered so far as it is practical because it represents something upon which they agree and which they enjoy together.

The importance of the ability of two partners in marriage to converse with one another is obvious. This is particularly true for the couple which has reached the stage of engagement. If two people have reached the engagement period and are unable to talk about important subjects in their future lives, it is doubtful that they will acquire this ability after marriage. They may have to have information pressed upon them and be cautiously, carefully, and, sometimes, painfully guided through numerous subjects by marriage counselors.

We are, of course, here concerned with the basic issue of communication. It is not unusual to find a serious lack of communication between two people who seem genuinely in love with one another and are rapidly approaching their marriage date; often they have not been able to communicate on the problems of sex, menstruation, pregnancy, children, or even money. A certain amount of charity and education are required for good communication. A large amount of trust is also necessary. Intellectual honesty will enable either partner to communicate his or her deep and sincere feelings on a personal and particular subject and receive the opinions of the other partner in return. This is the way it should be and the way everyone interested in marriage would like to see it be because this is the basis upon which decisions are easily and graciously made in marriage. The foundation for such success is most easily and gradually made prior to marriage. If such communication is not developed prior to marriage, perhaps the wedding should be postponed until it has developed or the reason for the lack of communication has been discovered and treated.

A somewhat different indicator of a successful marriage, which has been found to be generally reliable by all observers of the marriage state, is the communicative silence that occurs between two people genuinely in love. Sooner or later it becomes the subject of comment not only by the couple themselves but by observant friends and relatives. Where there is not a union "of true minds" and the personalities are not properly balanced, silence may become irritating, bitter, and separating. But two people really in love are satisfied merely to be near one another. Their silence is not only golden and communicative but, as the years go by, quite informative.

There are few things more edifying than a happy marriage of long standing. Such marriages are evident to those who merely look around in their families and circle of friends; those who never look for them seldom find them.

Any marriage counselor will vouch for the importance of carefully selecting a partner and the significance of a happy marriage and family. Firm home training provided by happy parents generally results in a happy childhood, and this is the firmest kind of a foundation upon which to build a personality which will be successful in marriage. The parents who provide the example of a happy marriage offer an indelible object lesson to the child in love, honor, and respect for the given word.

Just as experience has taught us the value of the factors mentioned above in the selection of a partner, surveys have also shown us certain warning signs. The following warnings indicate there are rough days ahead for a marriage and "look out" signs should be flying!

1. The husband-to-be's parents disapprove of the match. Unless the young couple can move a safe distance (roughly a thousand miles) there may be unceasing difficulties. It apparently is not too common for the bride-to-be's parents (her mother *may* be very active) to carry on such a concerted campaign as the husband-to-be's parents.

2. An indecisive male. Such a man is not really qualified to be the head of a house or the head of a family at least from an emotional point of view. Decisions have to be made in marriage, and experience has taught us that if the male is actually inferior, or feels that way, the problems are compounded.

3. Moody people. Moody or pessimistic people are not good material, to use a snobbish phrase, because they usually cannot supply that initial "good push" to victory or the will to win.

4. Selfishness. The heroic efforts on the part of one member of the partnership to get his or her own way in a determined fashion *all the time* indicate a degree of selfishness which is surmountable but not without soul-burdening work on the part of the beloved.

5. Marked differences in economic and social backgrounds. Differences in backgrounds, particularly if the female's is on a higher level than the male's, places an unwonted burden on the marriage itself.

6. Sexual misunderstandings. Premarital intercourse, because of the lack of respect involved; fear of sex and pregnancy because of the degree of ignorance involved; and an "excessively modest" attitude because of the no-trust attitude involved, all handicap a successful marriage.

7. Religious differences. As Jung pointed out many years ago, most people middle-aged or older who are properly oriented towards religion have fewer emotional problems, neurosis, and personality disturbances than those who are agnostic. Conversely, he said that the agnostics and atheists not only many times had serious problems, but the problems were relatively unsolvable because they failed to believe. It is not surprising then, although it is interesting, that successful marriages are difficult to come by where the background is irreligious, atheistic, or agnostic.

Analyses of successful marriages have elicited many reasons for their success. At least two are worth commenting on. 1. Successful marriages are made where great needs are satisfied—the great needs of companionship, affection, understanding, and love. It is worth pointing out that love includes the sexual act in the conjugal act of love, but a marriage, if necessary, can be held together without it. 2. One very cogent reason behind successful marriages is the confident expectation on the part of the two people involved that their marriage will be successful from the very outset.

With all our exploration of personality traits and certain aspects of the philosophy of the marriage partners, we always seem to return to the original question proposed by people genuinely in love: What can I do *for* you? This has sometimes been called the gift of giving. Persons who love one another give to each other anything they have, including— and especially—themselves. This ability to give to one another is indeed a blessing and is anyone's most precious wedding gift. But it must be remembered that it is a gift of personality, a gift of true minds. Thus, so accurately did Shakespeare put it:

Let me not to the marriage of true minds
Admit impediments. Love is not love
Which alters when it alteration finds,
Or bends with the remover to remove:
O, no! it is an ever fixèd mark,
That looks on tempests and is never shaken;
It is the star to every wand'ring bark,
Whose worth's unknown, although his height be taken.
Love's not Time's fool, though rosy lips and cheeks
Within his bending sickle's compass come;
Love alters not with his brief hours and weeks,
But bears it out even to the edge of doom:—
　If this be error and upon me proved,
　I never writ, nor no man ever loved.

4

Relationships With People:
The Engagement Period
and After

We have stressed repeatedly that two people who wish to marry should satisfy themselves that they can get along with one another, can come to an understanding on a number of important and basic subjects, and can establish a good personal and intimate relationship. In short, they have to determine in their own minds whether they are geared to enter into a give-and-take relationship.

After marriage, relationships with other people become almost equally important. There was a time when one of the chief problems of a newly married couple was their relations —in other words, in-laws. Well, in-laws are still with us. After marriage, everybody is somebody's in-law. This really means that everybody is someone's son or daughter, or mother or father, or sister or brother—the "in-law" is added for clarification. After marriage, our duties, responsibilities, and reactions to other people, whether they be friends, relatives, or neighbors, change considerably. These people are no longer to be met under more or less formal conditions, greeted according to a certain protocol, or engaged in conversational combat with rubber-tipped words. They are now guests to be entertained and relatives or friends who must be accepted as they are. With growing maturity, the newly-weds must sooner or later realize that the world is at least as broad as two families. Everyone can (or can try to) influence the attitudes of the people in the world about him, but the fact remains, we have to learn to live with people pretty much as they are.

As a rule, the first contact the maturing young adult has with the older world about him is when he or she begins to "go steady" or thinks seriously of becoming engaged. Then they begin to talk about "unwanted and unwarranted interference" on the part of families, relatives, and friends. Occasionally, when the question of an impending marriage is raised, some member of the family, or perhaps the entire family, raises objections. Under these circumstances, the wise young man or woman will listen, if for no other reason than out of filial devotion. Families generally have their members' best interests in mind.

Objections on the part of families or friends generally follow a pattern, which is apt to be repeated in various other contexts. The first question to ask is what type of objection does the family have? Is the objection based on age, money, education, social position, or that indefinable and rather snobbish term known as class? If so, these are at least specific reasons and the attitude of the parent, or relative, or friend is apt to be reasonable, whether or not the individual affected agrees. After all, it is reasonable to be concerned about an impending marriage in which the male partner has no likely means of support or has a past record of drifting, or incompetence.

There is a second general pattern of objection which is very revealing and can be significant for the future. Is the family objecting to a particular marriage or to marriages in general? In other words, is there an over-protective attitude in the objections of the family? Are their objections based upon blind thinking in which their only purpose, to use military parlance, is to fight a delaying action? The recognition of this pattern of thinking is important. It may lead the individual concerned to come to a bitter decision over what he or she considers the outrageous attitude of the family, but it will certainly alert both members of the partnership to the general pattern of thinking they may expect from the family in the future.

The third type of objection arising from families is born out of what is sometimes called a "match-making attitude." The objection of the family is based not so much on any specific feeling for the individual involved but on a substitute candidate whose value they would like to promote. This is ordinarily easily recognized by the people involved, but what is perhaps not so easily appreciated is that this attitude is one reason why some people acquire in-laws who are "the managing type."

In-laws or families tend to react in these ways because they are people and these are typical human reactions. But all this is more or less on the negative side. Why should potential in-laws object to a particular engagement? Is there something restive about the couple that seems dangerous to the families involved? Have relatives and friends been given reason to become involved with the problems and decisions of an individual couple? Do the couple have repeated episodes of indecision and petty bickering and show a basic inability to compromise? Actually, the best possible basis for getting along with other people and establishing a good relationship with them is a thorough, knowledgeable, and unselfish relationship between the partners.

The process by which any two couples go from acquaintanceship to marriage may differ markedly. The hand of Providence makes the road for one couple quick and easy, accompanied by a song of life and love, and for another slow and devious, with numerous bifurcations. In all cases, however, the move is from acquaintanceship to companionship.

Fortunately, most people instinctively realize that if companionship cannot be developed all thought of marriage is ridiculous. Companionship as a conscious state is much underrated. Few people realize that while acquaintanceship is replaced by companionship, love never replaces companionship; rather, it builds upon it. To feel a sense of being a companion to another individual is not like a set of aches and pains that make you "feel sick," nor is it the mere enjoyment of one another's company; it is the beginning of enjoyment of a mutuality of interests. Everyone has a few basic things in life with which he or she feels very comfortable. These are the things which must be explored at the companionship stage to see if they are identical or at least compatible to and acceptable to the prospective partner. If one finds enjoyment and relaxation when tired in playing a piano and in the same situation piano playing jangles the other's nerves, there is a strain on the prospective tie. If "Manon" and "Swan Lake" move one deeply and the other is addicted to professional wrestling, if one likes the theater and the other is captivated by melodramatic movies—then, however much they might like dining and dancing, swimming and skating together, the thread of companionship would be rather thin. This is important; people in love must be real companions, for as the years of common life broaden, their companionship becomes more and more obvious and more and more precious.

Kissing, Embracing, Necking, Petting

Each young person, when he reaches the appropriate age at which it is a social and proper thing to "date," discovers himself an adult. This discovery is as natural and dramatic as the young boy's discovery of shaving or the young girl's discovery of the advantages of sweaters. Boys and girls, when they discover the opposite sex, abandon their natural suspicion and hostility and find each other interesting and stimulating.

The opposite sex then, and sex itself, become subjects to be explored much as any new subject opens itself to the young mind. There are three major obstacles which the young person encounters under these circumstances. The first is the determination to prove himself or herself to be actually an adult and not simply one who has just undergone bodily changes signifying the beginning of adult life. They feel they must *think* as adults because they are *beginning* to think as adults. They have a determination to imitate and to act the part of adults and at times, in sheer bravado, to out-adult the adult.

The second obstacle which the young person must overcome in his dealings with the opposite sex is the fact that he or she is experiencing sensations or feelings or responding to stimuli that have never before been so powerful or so personal. These emotional feelings and stimuli, were they to admit it, are actually a little frightening and more than a little confusing. Coupled with the above-mentioned self-imposed mandate to act as an adult, the youngster frequently dares to do things which he or she doesn't really understand.

The third obstacle has to do with previous training. It is pounding the obvious to recall some facets of misconduct

traceable to lack of proper sex education—illegitimacy, homosexuality, venereal disease, etc. It needs to be stated and re-
iterated that proper attitudes toward sex are built in the
home, and lack of direction from the home leads to opinions
about sex in the young person's mind which vary from the
peculiar to the abnormal. By the same token, misdirection
in the home about sex can lead to a fear of sex—to anxieties,
guilt, scrupulosity, and a state of tension that carries fear
and even rejection to the conjugal act of love in marriage.

The young man or woman must be equipped with knowledge, understanding, and above all support. He needs someone to help him to be himself. He needs the benefit of others'
experience, not employed as medicine, but softly and gently
given as a catalyst to his own good thinking. The young person, because it is the nature of man, is groping for some
standard with which he can find some peace of mind in his
actions and upon which he can build his own philosophy of
life.

The teaching that has prevailed in education and psy-
chology in the last thirty years in too many instances has
denied the young person a standard. His teachers (and fundamentally his parents are his teachers), imbued with the "all-
wisdom" of permissiveness and learning by doing, have denied
him the support, understanding, and benefit of their experience, which he has fundamentally always wanted. The result
has been rebellion against authority and the chaotic state of
morality which we see around us.

Despite all this, anyone who works with young people
will tell you that in the area of sex youngsters constantly
want to know what is right and wrong. Because of the intensely personal, powerful, and sensually pleasurable nature
of sex, everyone discovers kissing, caressing, petting, and
necking as though it were something new, as though it had
never happened to anyone before.

Premarital behavior on dates has come to be known by a number of terms in this country. The most common term, which in a general sense is used to describe all forms of behavior on a date, is petting. Petting is generally defined as kissing, embracing, or hugging, and stroking or caressing the lips, face, or the erogenous areas of the body, which are chiefly the skin of the neck, the breasts, the inner areas of the thighs, and the genitals. Petting as a general term, then, includes all types of behavior up to but not including the actual act of intercourse. Its five behavioral forms include:

1. *Kissing:* Looked upon by some as the simplest form of sexual activity, it should be viewed as an expression of affection. A kiss is not a reward, nor should it be; it is not something done "for kicks" or because everybody else does it. A kiss as an indication of genuine affection in the beginning relationship between a boy and a girl should be innocuous and have something of beauty, tenderness, and consideration about it.

2. *Hugging or embracing:* Hugging should be an expression not only of affection but of joy. It should have no true sexual connotation and, like the kiss, may have no sexual significance at all. In general it can be said that kissing and embracing are the signs of lovers who have joy in one another's company as they get to know one another well and their friendship blossoms into love.

3. *Necking:* This is a colloquial term born of the American tendency to use language expressively. From surveys based on questionnaires given to young couples, it is obvious that, however anyone else may wish to define it, necking to young American couples of this generation refers to prolonged kissing and hugging which leads eventually to some degree of sexual stimulation. If it is

legitimate (and it is always dangerous) in any phase of premarital behavior, it may be reserved to the mature engaged couple. In anticipation of marriage, the joys of a common life, and the plans for a home, they may on certain occasions prolong their expression of love and joy with one another. But usually they recognize that such behavior is sexually stimulating and dangerous and, because they are mature and in love, they will stop before the practice becomes a personal danger to their own love.

4. *Light petting:* To most authorities, light petting is almost a theoretical consideration. It is something like starting off at the top of a ski jump—in the first few feet of the approach it is theoretically possible to stop oneself, but usually by the time one has gathered momentum in a ski jump, the jumper has gone all the way. Light petting refers to kissing, caressing, and stimulation of the erogenous areas of the body either through the clothing or next to the skin and involving the breasts, the skin of the thighs, and the genitals. Light petting is supposed to stop short of full sexual satisfaction or orgasm for either member of the partnership and certainly to stop short of intercourse.

All four of these categories—kissing, embracing, necking, and petting—have been produced by the inventive teenager as a substitute for sexual satisfaction and intercourse, *but they have long been recognized by all married people as the necessary elements of successful foreplay prior to the actual act of love.*

5. *Heavy petting:* Heavy petting is actually a substitute for sexual intercourse and is, therefore, *unnatural and immoral.* This is a scientific definition and one that is accepted by authorities who have studied the problem

and by couples who have been unhappy enough to succumb to the activity. Heavy petting involves manual stimulation of the genitals by one member of the partnership or by both to the point of sexual orgasm or complete sexual satisfaction. It has been called an intensely pleasurable adventure which entails no obligation or responsibilities. Those who indulge in it cheat on nature or attempt to do so by mutual masturbation for the crude bodily satisfaction and pleasure to be derived from it. This attempt to satisfy a bodily appetite in a crude animalistic sense employs a means which avoids the responsibilities of the act. Heavy petting is an insult to marriage and the marriage contract, whether it is done outside the marriage for sheer pleasure or inside marriage for contraception. It denies the natural function of the act itself, which is to serve the purpose of building a family and expressing the mutual love of the couple themselves.

In summary, heavy petting is immoral and unnatural. Light petting, as defined, is to a physician who has had some experience with people in their sexual lives, so little different from heavy petting as to be talking about the same thing. It, too, can only be condemned. Kissing, hugging, and caressing, in moderation, are a proper function of people who are beginning to share their love and have joy in the sharing. Necking, as defined, is dangerous for people because they are so very human but may be the occasional action of the engaged couple with sufficient self-control as the wedding draws near.

Surveys have been mentioned as a source of information. It is perhaps worth pointing out that surveys rarely are made to determine normal activities or to find out what normal, self-controlled people do. The emphasis is usually on the abnormal, the pathological, to discover how people deviate from accepted standards of behavior. Nevertheless, the surveys are interesting. They show us the reasons people give for indulging in petting, heavy and light. It is striking to note that the reasons given are almost completely divorced from the concept of the sexual act as an expression of love between married people.

In some cases, petting is a symbol of the rebellious spirit of the age group, a defiance of authority, both parental and other, which repeatedly warned against it. This legitimately may be taken as demonstrating a lack of what is called filial devotion; the spirit of family love and family unity has been so ignored in precept, teaching, and example that such youths have sought answers, self-expression, and entertainment outside the home.

Some youngsters gave as their reason for petting the fact that the entire group, fellows and girls, were all doing it or a desire to show they were not prudish. Men often cited as their motivation the attempt to prove masculinity; women said it was one way of becoming popular, or to prove that she was desirable and could capture a husband.

All too commonly, petting is initiated while under the influence of social pressures—alcohol, a sexual manner of dancing, or because everyone else is doing it. Occasionally a couple genuinely in love are simply carried away. In any event, petting indicates a lack of self-discipline, a lack of awareness that there is a standard of morality which, if society is to escape chaos, must be taught in the family and dutifully supported by each member. Heavy petting with its dodging of responsibility and the unnatural character of its performance is just another example of people doing things *to* one another; it carries no connotation of love, only of appetite. It attempts to divorce sex and love.

Any level of petting involving physical contact, from the

innocent to the dangerous, can, for any couple, become electrifying and dangerous. Every couple, regardless of how careful, will occasionally run into such difficulties and become concerned about the nature of their behavior. There are five commonly accepted rules by which dating behavior may be critically evaluated:

1. Stop whatever you are doing, if there is a sense of guilt afterwards. If you do not understand what you are doing—and this is possible—or you don't understand why you have feelings of guilt, then seek advice from someone you know and can trust, someone whose judgment you respect, someone who knows what you are talking about and is Catholic in spirit and in fact.

2. It is time to stop if there is a sense that whatever has been done on a date has created a real physical and emotional problem for the other partner; that is, he or she gets too excited and too quickly.

3. If there is enjoyment on a date *only* if there is physical contact, you should have further thoughts about this person before you seriously think of continuing the relationship or considering marriage.

4. If the sense of emotional and physical urgency seems to be in danger of spilling over and becoming uncontrollable (the party is getting rough), then quit. However, it is not sufficient merely to quit at that particular time; it is also necessary not to place yourself in the same position again.

5. If irritability and insomnia follow a date and the level to which you are being emotionally keyed is too high, the dating behavior should then be evaluated with your partner with a view to determine how your time together should be spent—it should be spent at least less passionately.

Steady Dating

We hear arguments, which often grow to violent proportions, at all levels of the community for and against steady dating. The biggest problem involves steady dating and the teenager. It is probably safe to say that most people agree that most teenagers are not ready for *steady* dating. Whether the teenager is basically selfish or is so preoccupied with his beginning awareness of himself that he is oblivious of the world around him (including the person whom he is dating and his or her family), is something of an academic dispute. In any case, most parents feel that the average teenager lacks the maturity to go steady.

It might be well perhaps to put it another way. The teenager who goes steady puts all of his curiosity and emotional drive into one individual at a time when that curiosity and emotional drive could readily encompass, and with great profit, an evaluation of many individuals. He loses an opportunity for knowledge which may never pass his way again. He leaves himself and his steady open to potential pain or even trauma should the association be suddenly or with finality broken.

There is little question that steady dating at too early an age leads to early marriage. Many a sailor has left port on the first ship going; in many instances he has done well, but he has never had the opportunity of seeing the other ships in port. At a young age physical awareness is something new and rather different, so exploratory and sometimes violent physical contacts occur in early steady dating. This may lead not only to early marriage but to pregnancy outside of marriage and occasionally to unwise marriages as well. Steady dating at an early age is likely to be done because it is the socially accepted custom in the community or as a new status symbol for the "liberated" young adult (the teenager). Steady dating should come only after exploratory dating has uncovered the field to disclose where indeed the daisies grow.

An old teacher of mine, speaking to a class of boys in high school, once pleaded with them never to marry a girl unless they could see her early in the morning at the breakfast table. She felt it would be a wonderful opportunity to see the girl as she was, without the benefit of the war paint. What she was really talking about of course, was the necessity for seeing the individual whom you may approach with a contract of marriage in some setting other than a glamorized dinner date, day at the seashore, or evening at the theater.

Perhaps Kipling said it best: " 'Tisn't beauty, so to speak, nor good talk necessarily. It's just IT. Some women will stand in a man's memory if they once walk down the street." Kipling's "It" has of course become legendary. He was not referring necessarily to sexual appeal in the crude sense of sex as it is known today, although this is the connotation often attributed to this quotation. Rather he seemed to be referring to sexual attractiveness or a compelling femininity that is a personal characteristic of everything most women do. It is a natural, unstudied womanliness that requires no artificial aids or assistance. It is enhanced by sincerity and cleanliness of spirit and shines through to everyone.

Most women insist that men have "It" also. This is a firm, clean-cut masculinity that shows itself in a natural poise, directness of approach, and a spontaneous honesty.

With this as a background a couple can move to explore companionship not merely by physical contact—or even by physical contact—but by what the song refers to as "getting to know you." The dating should involve home dates, at each partner's home, meeting the families, and getting to know something of the other's background, meeting each other at work, noting each other's friends and acquaintances, dating with mutual friends, and dating with one another's friends.

A couple should explore each other's family ties and ideas of family bonds; their ambitions, plans for the future, and political ideas. They should evaluate one another's religious feeling, courage, and honesty and discover one another's feelings for the theater, politics, and art. These things take time to accomplish but can be fun. No one suggests that these pursuits supplant the important physical contacts of dating. We do insist, however, that the pursuit of these subjects is necessary for an eventual happy marriage and far more important for the future happiness of a couple and their families than dates in which physical contact alone is pursued. Kissing and necking on a date can be lovely if transient, but it may be idly pursued; marriage is never transient and never idle.

And so as the couple approach the engagement they should have a companionship of which they are very sure, one that is solid and comfortable. They should have spent sufficient time building through their companionship a sense that the one thing that will make them happiest in life would be to give anything, including themselves, to each other. Once such a decision has been made, the engagement is in order.

The Engagement

The day of engagement is a solemn day, a solemn occasion in a couple's life together. It is also a day for pride because it signifies an individual's willingness to give and to receive the pledge of the person he or she loves most to start the long road of marriage together. It is a day of flattery, joy, and promise. And, considering the nature of marriage, it must, of necessity, be a day of great holiness.

It is interesting to see today the return of the solemn engagement, which was prevalent in the early Church. It is becoming popular, particularly in this country, to hold a small ceremony, usually in Church, in which the engagement ring is blessed and, on some occasions, a document is signed between the parties. This has its counterpart in the Roman *sponsalis* or betrothal ceremony (the marriage ceremony itself being called the Nuptiae) being, according to Roman law, a *consensus sponsalitus* or free engagement, a *pactum de contrabendo*, binding upon the contracting parties unless dissolved by mutual consent. As Roman law admitted an action for damage in the case of non-fulfillment so the Council of Elvira made persons liable to excommunication for three years in the event of a breach made after the *sponsalis*.

The first Christian marriages, therefore, supplemented the betrothal with the plighting of the troth, the nuptial ceremony, and the *subarrhatio* (the delivering of the *arrhae* pledges). These were accompanied by certain prescribed symbolic actions—the veiling of the bride, the crowning of the couple, the giving of the ring, and the handing over of the bride to the bridegroom in *focie ecclesiae* (inside the Church), followed by a solemn benediction as a part of the nuptial mass and the communion of the contracting parties. Eventually, the *sponsalis* was transformed from the civil ceremony into a *matrimonium* or sacramental ceremony. And for quite some time the *sponsalis*, the betrothal, and the marriage ceremony proper, the *nuptiae*, continued to be distinct observances.

As a part of the betrothal ceremony in Roman law, the promise of future marriage was ratified by the bestowal of an iron ring. This is an outgrowth of what was referred to as the *arrhae*. An *arrhae*, or earnest money, was a Roman custom of breaking gold or silver as a pledge of the marriage pact, and one half of the earnest money was kept by the woman and the other by the man. When the ring was finally substituted for the actual piece of gold or silver, iron was the metal selected and the iron ring was originally said to have been a link in an iron chain. At a much later date gold was substituted for the iron. Pliny, in 61-113 A.D., wrote that the gold ring was given in his time to the bride to wear in public and later another one of iron was given to wear indoors. Others say that heavy rings were worn in winter and lighter ones in summer. Tertullian, the Latin father of the Church, says that a ring of gold was used in ancient times. In any event, the betrothal ring or earnest money or *arrhae* was symbolic of a marriage by purchase and became the engagement ring of today.

The bridal shower, according to an ancient legend, originated many years ago in Holland. A beautiful young lady wanted to marry a miller, but the miller lacked wealth because he had always contributed to the poor of the village, so the lady's father selected a wealthy hog farmer as his future son-in-law instead. When the people of the village learned of the situation, they called upon all those who had received assistance from the miller over a period of years and marched to the bride's home carrying gifts of all sorts, making marriage possible.

The dowry also has a curious history. In the past, a man who wished to marry a young lady was expected to make a sizable contribution to the family. This has been somewhat wearily called "marriage by purchase." The development of a trousseau or a dowry was one way of compensating the future bridegroom for the money or goods which he gave the girl's father in payment for the daughter. Realizing the facts of the situation, most girls started early to collect linens, fine clothing difficult or tedious to make, and any other necessities which were time-consuming and hand-made. Superstition required that the girl not use any of these things before marriage or be doomed to the single life. The practical realities of marriage in years gone by prompted suitors to inspect and evaluate the "hope chest" before entering into negotiations to "buy" or obtain a wife.

There is also an old Greek custom which states that the sons of the family have to remain single until the daughters are married. Therefore, it became the custom for the sons to develop a dowry or hope chest and give to the girl all kinds of things which she could take into a wedding. Thus she became known early as a "real prize" for what she could bring as her dowry.

From the point of the engagement, love and romance, fiancé and home, and the building of a family should become the serious business of the day. Discussions should take on a new tenor now that certain basic points of agreement have been made and the couple have progressed to the point where they feel secure in their love and fidelity for one another.

It is in line with this thinking that the re-introduction of the solemn engagement has become most fitting and salutary. In this way, the couple profess their love solemnly before God and make public assurances to one another of their determination to make a happy marriage.

It is only natural in the course of an engagement that the couple be drawn closer together. The initiative for discussion, instead of being one-sided (usually started by the male as heretofore), is now shared on at least a fifty-fifty basis; the girl as well as the boy brings up subjects for discussion. Discussions on serious subjects should be encouraged by both partners, and they should be open to discover if their discussion of *any* subject can produce a base broad enough for compromise. This serves also to discover what pattern of prejudices either partner might have. These discussions, properly pursued in the course of a few short months, are effective in determining whether or not an engagement

should be pursued further. The following points should be
kept in mind:

1. If a partner avoids discussion of serious problems, for
   example, religion and children, the situation is potentially dangerous. No successful marriage can be based
   on one-sided conversation. Communication at least
   shows interest; it is stimulating, it can be irritating, but
   usually it results in a solution to a problem. If someone
   avoids discussion of a subject it indicates indifference
   and apathy, and such an association can be frustrating.
2. On the other hand, an individual with strong, resolute,
   and unbending ideas and attitudes about important subjects can also be a difficult person with whom to spend
   one's married life. Strong-minded individuals are valuable assets to society. They make society move, and they
   make family society interesting. The strong-minded individuals who are also stubborn are usually so en-
   trenched that there is no motion and no progress.
3. Discussions soon make obvious the ability or inability
   to make an independent decision. If the authority for
   statements, behavior, or plans is usually a person, and
   a particular person at that, then there may be rough
   days ahead. Too frequently in such instances the
   authority is mother, father, brother, or some other person
   who is always consulted and whose decision is always
   borrowed. As you enter into marriage, you want your
   partner's decisions, right or wrong, because they are the
   only ones that are important, and in the long run it is
   their influence in common decisions with which you have
   to live.
4. If a person has become engaged as the result of pressures from relatives, friends, and/or circumstances, free
   discussion during the period of engagement will soon

make this obvious. If a girl has become engaged to a boy out of desperation and because "he is a good boy," thorough discussion of a number of subjects will show a lack of spontaneity and an interest which is almost casual about things that are vitally important to a married couple. This is not an altogether unwholesome philosophy or attitude to bring into marriage, except that in this instance it will be the *only* attitude brought into marriage since the love which can keep things simple, organized, and directed is missing.

5. The engagement period is an excellent opportunity to get to know one another's habits as well as possible. There are three habits which make living together well-nigh intolerable. The first is alcoholism, which so alters the personality as to destroy the security and the personal relationships in marriage. The second is gambling, which usually seriously undermines the economic security of the home; at the same time it destroys the trust between one another. The third is flirting, which is an assault on the marriage contract itself. If one partner persistently attacks the fidelity two people in marriage give to one another, then the beauty of the common life is destroyed. These three habits, then, if discovered to be ingrained seriously in the personality of the individual prior to the marriage, should make one pause seriously and consider breaking the engagement.

6. In breaking an engagement, the individuals involved should think only of the genuine character of their love for one another. If the individuals feel that their love is strong, clean, unencumbered by doubts of fidelity, and unfettered by the problems mentioned above, then they are on solid ground. On the other hand, if any of the problems mentioned above are real, then the couple should realize that breaking the engagement may be

necessary. Under these circumstances such a step is probably the adult, reasonable, and thoroughly correct thing to do. In the presence of grave doubts about a prospective partner, one must bear in mind always that marriage is for real and until death. Should the engagement be broken, there should be no qualms based upon unpleasant publicity or the thought that people may gossip. It should be remembered that a bad marriage will eventually result in far worse publicity, far more talk—and rather permanent unhappiness as well.

Relationships with Family, Friends, In-laws

In a couple's first five years of married life, their families and friends tend to be liberal with advice, which is usually given along three lines—a reasonable attitude, an unreasonable attitude, or a managing "let me take over" attitude. Here are a few guiding rules which may help to make this relationship of family, in-laws, or friends more bearable and somewhat less confusing:

1. The younger in-laws (or friends), that is, within a ten to twenty-year difference in age, the more interfering they are likely to be. Younger people tend to be more dogmatic; they often feel that having been through something once they know all the answers. It is probably true that personality differences notwithstanding, where the age difference between the newly-weds and their in-laws is thirty or more years, the younger ones find more discreet silence, listening, and encouragement rather than management and dogmatism. By the same token, the younger the couple, that is, the newly-weds, the greater the conflict is apt to be between a strong

desire to assert an independence newly acquired and to maintain close ties of dependence.

2. Never participate in exclusive planning with a sister, brother, mother, or father. There is nothing more irritating to one member of a partnership than to be faced with a *fait accompli* which has been executed by mother and daughter, or sister and sister, or father and son. Newly-weds, like any other couple new to any type of enterprise, are never going to be able to make intelligent plans or reasonable decisions until they have gone through the mill of decision together. This is really what the first five years of marriage are for. The early years of marriage are not for the mother to tell her daughter everything she has learned in twenty-five years; the daughter may not want to learn those things. By the same token, except for business and professional advice (which, by the way, the older man is rather loath to give), the first years of married life are not for the father to use as a cramming session to offer his son his solution to problems.

3. Don't move in with in-laws. If there is one universal opinion of marriage counselors (and I might add, of most mature women) concerning marriage, it is this: it is an exceedingly big house that can take two women. The consensus of opinion is that all newly-weds should have a place of their own even if it is a single room. It isn't necessarily a matter of one woman getting along with another in the same house, although this is a major problem; it is more importantly a matter of newly-weds having a place in which they can move around, think, plan, and develop on their own early in marriage.

4. The telephone company is constantly pointing out the advantages of the telephone and how near it can make

people who are really near and dear to all of us but who are some distance away. The telephone may also become an instrument of inquisition. Many a newly-wed couple has been badgered by the daily inquiring in-law, friend, or relative who must have a blow by blow description of the previous twenty-four hours so that he or she can contribute free advice. This can not only become annoying but actually confusing. Some means, even a direct invitation to stop the practice, should be taken to control it.

5. Pampering of a couple by in-laws or favorite relatives is good only up to a certain point. That point, it might be added, is a very short one in the course of marriage. In general, the best way of fostering independence on the part of people is to force them, at least partially, to the point of independence. Since the average newly-weds, full of ambition and the desire to win, ought to be able to achieve their goals through their own re-sources and ingenuity, it is a mistake for in-laws or relatives of means to constantly offer financial help. This is not merely killing with kindness. If it persists, it stifles ambition, destroys self-respect, and creates serious difficulties.

6. Whether they will it or not, people have to train them-selves to evaluate other people. In-laws are no exception to this. The newly-wed couple must evaluate their in-laws, relatives, and friends on an educational and social level. They must bear in mind certain national habits or traits which are not changeable. They must, if they are fair, judge them on every other basis. This does not mean that one has to be a personality accountant, but it does mean that one has to take a serious view of the people who, in a small, partial sense, one is also marry-

ing. Once the evaluation has been made, always leaving room for the fact that you may be wrong, love as
you can, like what is wholesome, solid, and admirable,
and accept what you cannot understand.

7. Whatever the problem may be, always make an earnest
and repeated effort to attempt to solve your own problems first before seeking advice.

Essentially, the problems of dealing with people in the
early days of marriage are usually concerned with the matter
of advice. A young married couple, particularly one involved
in acquiring furniture or property, building a home, starting
a family, or doing all of these simultaneously, will run into
daily problems in which decisions will have to be made.
They discuss the matter seriously and as completely as time
will allow. Often they cannot discuss it repeatedly because
of time limitations, so in an effort to reassure themselves,
they seek advice. The darkest spot is directly beneath the
candle, and young people, under these circumstances, quickly
find themselves within the darkness.

If advice is sought, the first qualification to look for in the
advisor is that he or she be a good listener. The best advice
comes from those who never give advice at all but know how
to listen and how to evaluate the alternatives involved in
such a way that you can intelligently make up your own
mind. The second qualification for an advisor is that he or
she knows far more about the subject than you do.

These two qualifications could be developed in great
length, but they are perhaps best summarized as follows: In
seeking advice, seek the "old pros." The clergyman who has
seen a lot of people come and go, has heard everything a
hundred times, and has seen more fear and confusion than
he likes to remember is generally well-equipped and in an

excellent position to offer you advice on moral and ethical problems. Often he is well-equipped to give you advice on the art of living as well. However, like most professional people, he may be acting under two handicaps; he may have become dogmatic in matters other than those of morals and religion, and he may know all the parties involved in the dispute too well to be unprejudiced.

The physician also has seen a lot of living. He is best equipped, of course, to answer questions regarding health, present a proper outlook to various diseases, and give advice on problems that deal with medical facets of marriage. He, too, is in danger of becoming dogmatic from habit, and he also may know the persons concerned too well to be unprejudiced. Lawyers, accountants, social workers, psychologists all have their special fields, their special interests, their special abilities to offer advice. As already indicated, it is perhaps best to seek professionals, especially those who can listen and who have an ability to "lay on the table" more clearly the alternatives involved. Friends, for example, rarely listen in a matter leading to productive decision. A friend is generally afraid to give advice or is likely to misconstrue your request to talk something over to mean a request to take over. With few exceptions, at best the friend is a gifted amateur, is prejudiced on your side as a rule, and is necessarily subjective in his approach.

The term "professional" has been mentioned several times in the previous paragraphs. At least twice there has been the warning that they tend to be dogmatic. This deserves some comment. The professional, by whom we mean the serious student of a particular field, must and eventually does come to rather strong opinions. A physician cannot have any confidence in himself, or gain his patient's confidence, if he is not strong-minded. A balanced outlook in which the professional maintains his own self-confidence and forsakes the sharpened edge of extreme opinion takes time to acquire. So, a person seeking advice who can turn to an individual who has grown somewhat mellow within his profession and has seen enough of life to have few violent opinions is indeed fortunate. His comfortable air of talking and listening soon makes it easy for anyone to make his or her own decision.

In any case, make a habit of keeping the solution of your personal problems to yourselves. If the union which you have made with another individual is so close and personal, and you feel it can bring you closer to God, you should be able to come closer to that individual and manage your own problems, with or without expert advice from other sources, under your own roof. If this becomes a habit between the two of you, it is something that you can teach your children. One of the best ways of teaching your child the sanctity of the home is to show him that in the home everything may be talked about, and that those things which are peculiar to the home remain there, and that the best decisions are made at home.

It is important for all newly-married couples to be reminded that they have a right to make their own mistakes. In anything so personal as starting a marriage, a family, or raising a baby, mistakes are going to be made. It is a reflection on the remarkable Providence of God that so few serious mistakes are made by people acting on their own. And when mistakes are made, they are often the result of innocent, well-intentioned advice given by some amateur. Possibly the same advice in other circumstances, for other people, at another time, might have been quite correct. But, if it has proven wrong in this particular case, the recipients may harbor a certain amount of resentment towards the person who gave it. This becomes all the more important and cogent when the problem involved affects the matters of early marriage, of pregnancy, or a newborn baby. So, it is probably not wise to seek advice on these subjects from members of the family. By the same token, the members of the family should be reluctant to give advice on such problems to a young married couple.

To sum up, if advice is needed, it should be taken from professional sources, weighed carefully, and additional advice sought from additional sources if necessary. After due consideration, the two people involved should make the decision on their own. Once the decision is made, if it turns out correctly, they feel happy about the situation, they have learned something, and they gain confidence. If, on the other hand, their decision does not turn out well, they have learned something by their own mistake—what not to do in a given situation and why. In the course of human education, many times the most important things to learn are the things not to do and when not to do them.

In this way, two people, should they make mistakes, have no one to blame but themselves. And, as a rule, they will not have made a serious mistake because well-thought-out answers are rarely totally incorrect. But perhaps the most important consideration is the serious training they get by beginning their lives by making decisions based upon careful consideration of advice from all sources. This is the start of the formation of adult opinions and the assumption of adult responsibility.

In summary, the young couple should preserve their identities, physically, sexually, socially, emotionally, and intellectually until they have satisfied themselves that each knows the personality and character of the other thoroughly —and approves. Once they have made a firm judgment that their approval is so compelling as to be love, they are prepared to let bodies, minds, and hearts complement one another in marriage. Thus is the common life—so firm and faithful, steadfast and solid and dearly wished—placed in the reach of lovers.

5

Legal and Ecclesiastical
Regulations
Governing Marriages

Marriage is the means by which the family is introduced into society. Since the continued development of society depends on the family, it is obviously *the unit* of society. The family is the means by which the tenor, the ideals, and the traditions of a community, nation, and society are successfully passed from one generation to another. The parent has not only a natural mandate but a natural instinct for the care and training of the child. The directing, educating, and protective function of the parents shows the children how to live together and with others—a philosophy of life which no school can supply and no successful society can do without.

The matter of living in and with family, relatives, friends, neighbors, and community requires cooperation and a common agreement on purposes and principles of action. To protect these purposes and principles and the family as the unit of society, the state has developed laws regarding property, civil rights, and marriage.

A supernatural influence in the life of a man and woman together in marriage has always been recognized. Thus, religion has always had an interest, an influence, and a regulatory power with regard to the marriage contract. This is particularly true within the Christian religion. If we maintain, as we do, that our main theme is that we are on our way back to God, and the path that we have chosen is to help us to get there, then the protective role of religion in guarding and guiding marriage becomes obvious.

The state may make laws, in fact, *must* make laws, for the good of society, to regulate marriage, provided these laws do not violate the nature of marriage. If unbaptized people do not observe these laws, their marriage is not a marriage. The state may make laws concerning baptized people, again with the provision that these laws do not violate the nature of marriage or the laws of the Church. Marriage is a sacrament, and when baptized people enter into marriage validly they receive the sacrament of matrimony, over which the Church has sole jurisdiction. So, the Church makes laws concerning baptized persons in marriage. The Church law cannot violate the nature of marriage or the nature of a sacrament. Therefore, a close study of the Church's Canons or laws of marriage shows them to be largely a declaration of the truth of the matter; that is, the true nature of marriage, and the true nature of the sacrament, and the steps that must be taken for the protection of both. The laws of the state pertaining to marriage, which apply to all marriages between people both baptized and unbaptized, fall into practical, social, political, and public health categories.

Legal Regulations

The first legal regulation concerns eligibility for marriage. The conditions vary, of course, throughout the world, and even from state to state in the United States. In general, marriage is forbidden to those who are not mentally capable of entering into a contract. For example: the person who is disoriented as to time, place, and person due to drugs, mental illness, or intoxication is ineligible for marriage. Marriage is forbidden in many states for those who are impotent. The law forbids anyone from having more than one husband or wife. Many states have laws against common-law marriages wherein two people enter into a marriage-like relationship without benefit of the assistance of either the state or the Church. Some states have laws against marriages between people of different races. Marriage is forbidden by law among people who are related in a direct line (the incestuous marriage) and in most cases of people who are related collaterally, *e.g.,* first cousins.

The second legal regulation concerns age. The age at which people may marry varies in all parts of the world. As far as the United States is concerned the most common legal age is sixteen for the girl and eighteen for the man. Canon law makes it fourteen for the girl and sixteen for the man but this is a tradition; the Church definitely does not recommend, certainly in this day, that people marry at that age. In fact in this regard the Church *generally* follows the current civil law. The consent of the parent is required in the extraordinary circumstances in which marriage is undertaken by two people one of whom, at least, is under legal age. This consent must be presented to the license bureau.

The third legal requirement is a health certificate. An increasing number of states now require that prior to marriage the man and the woman show a certificate offering proof that within a ten-, thirty-, or sixty-day period before the marriage the couple were found to be free from venereal disease.

In every state, a couple who wish to be married must apply for a license. A license costs several dollars and usually application must be made in the location where the girl lives, unless the parties are away from home. One reason for obtaining a license is so the clerk of the marriage bureau may check on the eligibility for marriage, health certificate, age, parents' consent if necessary, and freedom from pre-existing marriage. Another reason is to afford the state a complete registration of those people who have married for the census, income tax purposes, and problems of inheritance. The waiting period is obviously set up so any pertinent information that is required by the license bureau may be obtained, and also for the very curious but human reason that a number of couples in a burst of enthusiasm rush down to get a license to marry but within a few days change their minds.

Despite the fact that the above precautions are taken by the state, it is not uncommon to find particular localities in which the waiting period may be waived. Such localities attract the irresponsibles—at any rate, in such communities marriage can be contracted unwisely and in haste. Consequently, it is possible for the state to find, on proper investigation, that some individuals, are not properly married because they were not eligible to marry, and, therefore, no true marriage resulted. Where people enter into a union where no marriage results, then a declaration of nullity (a statement that no marriage had ever existed as the result of the "ceremony") can be offered by the state. The most common causes for annulment are those mentioned before as the ones which make people ineligible for marriage—incest, intoxication, mental illness, lack of proper age, previous marriage, forced intoxication, and fraud.

Legal separation is a step taken in law where serious problems occur in a marriage and divorce is impossible. The term legal separation is much discussed in Catholic circles because it is the only legal step which Catholics can take in an impossible situation.

You cannot "escape" an impossible situation. You can move for a legal separation only with the approval of the Bishop of the Diocese and after a separation has been granted by the Church. The term legal separation formerly was called a separation from bed and board or even a divorce from bed and board, but it never has, and does not now, carry with it the connotation that the marriage is dissolved.

"This does not remove the wedding ring from the finger where it was placed when the solemn vows were exchanged; but the ring after the entry of the decree is a reminder of the restrictions which arise out of the relationship. The decree withholds from the offending spouse rights which previously were his and releases the guiltless spouse from the performance of duties previously owed."

—Alexander Lindey

"A legal separation has the effect of a divorce only to the extent provided by statute and is synonymous with a limited divorce. A legal separation differs from absolute divorce in that the parties are not free to marry any third person; the name of the wife cannot be changed; the parties may at any time resume the marital relations after filing a written declaration of such resumptions with the clerk of the Superior Court for the county in which the separation was decreed."

—A New Hampshire Decree of Separation

It must be remembered that:

1. Not every state recognizes a legal separation. (Ten states do not.)
2. The grounds allowed for a separation vary greatly within several states.
3. Adultery is not accepted as the grounds for separation in many states.
4. In some states, a legal separation is a preliminary step in all divorce actions as, for example, Louisiana. Catholics, of course, can take only this preliminary step.

There may be, under rare circumstances, an instance in which, for the preservation of property rights or some other legal right and where legal separation is not permitted, a *civil divorce* is necessary for Catholics. Such a situation is not common in the United States today, and in most states it is almost unknown. However, if it becomes necessary, permission for a civil divorce action must be obtained from the Bishop of the Diocese, and *it is obtained with the understanding that there is no recognition by the Church or the parties involved that the civil action has dissolved the marriage.* If a marriage is declared null and void (no marriage) by the Church, such a couple is required to go through a civil divorce ceremony lest, should they contract a valid marriage later on, they be considered bigamous under the civil law.

In summary, even though the laws of several states may vary the Supreme Court has ruled that a marriage which is valid in one state according to its laws and regulations is thereby to be considered valid in other states. For the same reason, divorce or a declaration of nullity which is legal, if properly determined by the laws of one state, shall be recognized by the other forty-nine.

Canon Law

The Church also has laws and the power to formulate laws on the regulation of marriage. In Canon 1016 of *The Code of Canon Law,* it says that the marriage of baptized persons is governed not only by Divine law but also by Canon law without prejudice to the competency of civil law as regards the merely civil effects of such marriage. The essential feature of marriage is the marriage contract. Canon 1081 says: "Marriage is effected by the consent of the parties lawfully expressed between two persons who are capable according to law, and this consent no human power can supply." Secondly: "Matrimonial consent is an act of the will by which each party gives and accepts a perpetual and exclusive right over the body for acts which are, of themselves, suitable for the generation of children." At the same time, as has been pointed out, the contract of marriage sets up a relationship between the two individuals which is bonded together by God Himself, and it is this relationship that makes a marriage a contract and sacrament. In Canon 1012 it is stated: "It is impossible for a valid contract of marriage between baptized persons to exist without being by that very fact a sacrament."

The catechism defines a sacrament as an outward sign instituted by Christ to give grace. The outward sign of the sacrament of marriage is the extreme show of consent by which the partners make a contract to give themselves to each other until death. The grace that comes from the sacrament of marriage is open to the partners as they, the ministers of the sacrament, themselves become channels of grace, one to the other.

If the outward sign is the exchange of consent given by

the partners to give themselves to each other, some consideration of consent and what it means should be made here.

1. Consent presupposes the use of reason. Thus, those who are insane, drugged, hypnotized, intoxicated, or those who have not reached the age of reason cannot give consent and cannot enter into marriage.

2. The person has to know the essentials of marriage, that is, that marriage is a contractual union between a man and a woman for the purpose of procreating children and is binding until death. It is presumed that such a person knows the facts of life and that a couple must enter into the bodily union known as the sexual act. A person who reaches sexual maturity, or puberty, as it is sometimes called, is presumed to understand these things. On the other hand, if it can be established that a person enters into marriage without any knowledge of what he or she is getting into, then no marriage can occur.

3. For consent the individual must have certain knowledge of the person he is marrying. This refers to the rare situation in which someone is marrying one of identical twins. The person who marries such an individual must have absolute knowledge that this is the individual he intends to marry. He cannot give consent to marry anyone else than the one whom he purports to marry.

4. There must be no pretense in the consent. The person going through a marriage ceremony is considered to know what he means and to mean what he says. It is, as a matter of fact, extremely difficult to prove that a person who has gone through a marriage ceremony was actually pretending except, of course, in the case of a person who was involved in a play or some make-believe situation wherein it is apparent to all present that no real marriage is taking place.

5. True consent presumes that no force or fear has been employed in obtaining such consent. Canon 1087 says:

"Invalid is the marriage entered into through force or grave fear unjustly inspired from without such that in order to escape from it a party is compelled to choose marriage." No other fear, even if it furnishes the cause for the contract, entails the nullity of marriage. Obvious, irresistible force which brings a person into marriage makes such a marriage null and void because the consent is not a true and freely given one. The fear must be serious and grave, must come from some other person, and it must be unjust. It, furthermore, must be of such a nature that the only way to escape it is to marry.

6. The consent must thoroughly intend the contract of marriage. Thus, if a party consents to marriage but denies at the same time that marriage is a contract, that is, is binding on both partners, and that such a contract gives the right to sexual intercourse, the individual does not really understand what marriage is and the marriage is invalid. It is impossible to make a contract where you believe no contract exists. If, on the other hand, a person so believes and enters into marriage believing that there is a contract, but has no intention of fulfilling the nature of the contract, the marriage is still valid.

In order to protect the contract and fulfill it properly so that two people may assist one another in this return back to God, certain laws have been instituted by the Church pertaining to the form of marriage itself.

To make a marriage valid, therefore, there must be not only a contract freely entered with consent freely given by people who are capable of giving such consent but such a marriage must also be celebrated before a bishop or pastor or by a priest delegated by either one and before at least two witnesses (according to Canon 1094). If the people who are getting married consider that the contract they are entering is holy and permanent, a means of salvation one for the other, then they should want to proclaim such a contract properly and proclaim its holiness before God and man. It is not unusual, therefore, that the Church should feel strongly about individuals who elect to "get married" in open defiance of this law of the Church. The marriage of two Catholics before a Justice of the Peace is no marriage at all, and in some dioceses incurs a reserved censure that cannot be removed by an ordinary confessor but only by the Bishop. A mixed marriage performed by a Protestant minister is not only invalid but also entails excommunication for the Catholic party; again, in some dioceses this is a reserved censure.

Many of the requirements which by civil law make a person ineligible for marriage will also make the same person ineligible for marriage by Church law. According to civil law the authorities state that there are some conditions under which two people cannot marry from the very nature of marriage itself. The Church also maintains certain prohibitions which spring from the very nature of marriage itself; it adds others which stem from the sanctity of marriage itself and the holy nature of the contract, and still others which from her experience and the experience of mankind have been shown to be real threats to the perpetuation of a successful marriage. These last prohibitions, however, are not contradictory to the essence of marriage itself and, therefore, a dispensation from them may be granted for grave and sufficient reason.

All of these prohibitions are classified as impediments. An impediment is an obstacle which may make marriage null and void, render it invalid, or make it difficult of practical summation. A dispensation may be granted to some types of impediments but not to others. The dispensation is the relaxation of a law for good and sufficient reason. No dispensation, however, may be granted for anything that involves the essence of the marriage contract itself. Dispensations are granted on the merits of the situation; they cannot be obtained by influence or fee. Always see your pastor for details regarding dispensations.

There are two types of impediments. The first is known as the *diriment impediment.* A diriment impediment is one which renders any attempt at marriage null and void; it is, therefore, sometimes known as an annulling impediment. The second impediment is called an *impeding* or *prohibitory impediment.* If marriage takes place in the face of such an impediment and all other conditions have been fulfilled, the marriage is valid but illegal or illicit.

The Diriment Impediments

Impotence. This means, very simply, the inability to perform the marriage act. An impotent person cannot fulfill the contract of marriage. Therefore, an impotent person, if the impotence exists at the time of marriage and is permanent (cannot be cured), can never marry. Under such conditions, such a marriage would be declared null and void because the essence of the contract is violated; the impotent person has nothing to give in the contract.

Impotence should not be confused with sterility. A considerable number of people marry who are sterile but potent. One out of six marriages in the United States is infertile, either because the woman has blocked tubes or is not ovulating regularly, if at all, or because the husband produces sperm which are not alive, insufficient in number, or not motile; these people are potent, but they are sterile, and they are, of course, validly married.

Previous valid marriage. If the other partner in a previous valid marriage is still living and if no competent authority can dissolve the bond, a diriment impediment exists which renders any attempt at union null and void. In very, very, very rare circumstances that shall be discussed later, the Pope can dissolve a non-consummated valid marriage and the original marriage of non-baptized persons by virtue of The Pauline Privilege. In general, *no dispensation* may be granted.

Blood relationship. When it occurs in the direct line, it is a diriment impediment. No dispensation is ever granted. Thus, a man cannot marry his mother, daughter, or grand-daughter. In a *collateral* line the impediment extends through the third degree inclusive. Thus, in the first degree, dispensation is never granted; a man cannot marry his sister. Second degree of kinship would be first cousins; third degree would be second cousins. Dispensation may be granted in the third degree if there is good reason.

Lack of consent or lack of understanding of the essence of marriage. Where a person cannot make a consent, as the child before the use of reason or the person who is not mentally competent, or where there is violent abduction, no dispensation may be granted.

Legal adoption. This is considered by some governments to be a diriment impediment, and in those countries where this attitude prevails it is adopted by the Church. It is a diriment impediment not by the nature of marriage but under Church law itself. Thus, a dispensation may be granted under some circumstances.

Age. The age required under Canon 1067 is sixteen for the man and fourteen for the woman. As mentioned above, however, the Church generally follows the civil law. The Church knows the difficulties that may arise from marriages entered into at such ages—or even above them—so places an impediment of age to declare a marriage null and void. However, under exceptional circumstances, it may grant a dispensation.

Disparity of worship. By disparity of worship is meant the attempted marriage between a Catholic and a non-baptized person. Non-baptized people are, of course, Jews, Mormons, non-baptized Protestants, Hindus, and Moslems. Because, religiously, such a couple have *no* common ground and strong and disparate religious feelings a dispensation is very rarely granted.

Sacred Orders: The marriage of a subdeacon, deacon, priest, or Bishop is invalid. The impediment that applies here is the vow or freely assumed obligation of chastity. Solemn vows likewise render an attempt at marriage null and void. Dispensation may be granted.

Violence. If a woman is detained without her consent by a man who under violence or threat of violence attempts to force marriage upon her, there exists a diriment impediment. According to Canon 1074 there can be no marriage so long as she remains within his control. This is technically known as abduction. If, however, when the woman is free she willingly agrees to enter into the marriage, the impediment ceases to exist.

Relationship by marriage or affinity. This makes an attempt at marriage between a married person and the blood relative of the spouse null and void. Thus, if one member of the marriage should die, the diriment impediment would exist between the remaining partner and his or her sister—or brother-in-law. *Dispensation may be granted.*

"Common law" marriage. Canon 1078 sets up an impediment of public propriety which involves a man and woman living together though not validly married. The Canon states that this impediment invalidates a marriage in the first and second degree of the direct line between the man and the blood relatives of the woman, and vice versa. A dispensation may be granted for just cause. This impediment however does *not* forbid the marriage of the parties themselves if no other impediment to their marriage exists.

Spiritual relationship. This is an impediment that exists

between a baptized person, the baptizer, and the God-parent. Dispensation may be granted.

There are other diriment impediments set by ecclesiastical law. Sacred order of the priesthood, affinity in the direct line where the marriage has been consummated, and crime including murder which has not become public are uncommon diriment impediments. (Dispensation is never granted for crime, including murder of the spouse, which has become public.) Because these impediments derive from Canon Law, dispensations theoretically may be granted, and occasionally are.

Impeding or Prohibitory Impediments

If marriage takes place in the face of a prohibitory impediment, and all other conditions for the marriage have been fulfilled, the marriage is valid but illegal or illicit. Thus, marriage in the face of a prohibiting impediment indicates that the person committed a grave sin by getting married under circumstances where marriage is forbidden. There are three prohibitory impediments:

1. *The simple vow of chastity.* This is relevant for people who make a private or simple vow of virginity, take Holy Orders, or any vow whose fulfillment is incompatible with the married state. Under appropriate circumstances and for good reason, dispensation may be granted.
2. *Legal adoption.* If there is a civil law that renders invalid a marriage between people who have a relationship in adoption, the Church agrees and under these circumstances places a diriment impediment to marriage.
3. *Mixed religion.* This impediment is the one *most commonly listed on applications for dispensation* in this

country. By the same token, it is one impediment that is most *commonly granted a dispensation* in this country. By mixed religion one means here that both partners are baptized, but one is a Catholic and the other is not, or one is a Catholic and the other is a presumably or doubtfully baptized non-Catholic. It is perhaps well to point out that mixed marriages get no formal benediction from any group of marriage counselors or any ministers of organized religions. There was a time when the Catholic Church was almost, but not quite, unique in the Western world in protesting about mixed marriages. At that time, the Church was criticized for taking a one-sided attitude towards a mixed marriage in requiring that three conditions be fulfilled prior to the Catholic being given a dispensation for a mixed marriage. Now, however, it is generally realized that the Church was wise in such an attitude, and more and more religious sects are opposing the intermarriage of people of different faiths. The reasons, of course, are compelling and obvious. If marriage is to be considered a means of salvation for the people involved, and the partners cannot agree on this one fundamental aspect of salvation, then the partners who should be so close, at least *on this one important subject,* are strangers and will remain so.

Even among the Protestant sects, for example, the Jehovah's Witnesses, the Mennonites, and the Seventh Day Adventists are considered somewhat unorthodox and, therefore, represent something of a religious hazard in a marriage to another Protestant. Marriages involving the traditional or conservative Episcopalian, the rather stern Lutheran, and the ultraliberal Unitarian are causing growing concern among Protestant leaders. And yet, as we will see, mixed marriages among all groups of people, within the Protestant denominations, and between Protestants and Catholics, seem to be on the increase. It might be fruitful to pause for a moment to consider some of the reasons why.

A. In some areas of the country, the distribution of Catholics and non-Catholics in the population makes some incidence of mixed marriages inevitable.

B. Some people are naturally inept in their relations with others and do not think of the consequences of fostering and continuing a relationship, whether it be in business, marriage, or social life. Thus, acquaintance to friend to fiancé to spouse.

C. Some people marry not for love but for a position or personal accomplishment. They give no more consideration to religion than they give to love itself.

D. As any young lady of eligible age will tell you, in most communities in the country, there are more women of eligible marriage age available than men. Women also tell us, and there is no social study that contradicts this, that in every community a certain percentage of girls are desperate for a man and determine to marry any man who is reasonably socially acceptable, has a pleasant personality, and offers them some security. Again there is no real consideration given to religion because there is no real consideration given to the selection of a marriage partner. Fundamental aspects of personality, love, and religion are ignored. The panicky reaction is to get married. It seems to matter little to whom.

E. Some people are chronically dissatisfied with anything they have; they are convinced that the grass in anyone else's backyard is greener. These are the people who tend to want to "lose their background;" they constantly seek complete change. Change is what is important to them—not considerations of love, religion, or the future. In a certain sense, these are the gamblers among us. Sometimes they are lucky and things work out very well—but only sometimes.

F. Another group of people who wish to be known as "creative" (in reality they are generally the "poseurs"), inventive, or daring seek others like themselves, and they seem to take almost a pride in the fact that they know little of the background or any of the important things about a prospective mate. In the parlance of the day these people are considered "sick."

The requirements for a dispensation for a mixed marriage are as follows:

1. A just and serious reason; for example, the girl is already pregnant prior to the marriage.
2. The signing of the promises involved in the ante-nuptial contract that the religion of the Catholic party and children will be safeguarded.
3. The moral certainty that the promises will be fulfilled as contained in Canon 1061. This again, as with the case of disparity of worship, is a stumbling block of the dispensation for mixed marriages—the moral certainty that the guarantees will be fulfilled. This brings to mind once again the fundamentals of the selection of a partner. The person, the personality, his or her upbringing, training, traditions, prejudices, and firm beliefs—these are the

factors that allow the priest and the individual involved to decide with some degree of certainty whether the promises can or will be kept. In the problem of mixed marriages we find usually an almost incurable optimism. This is not to say that mixed marriages have not been successful, holy, or happy—they have. But they are successful, holy, or happy in spite of the disparity of cult— not because of it. Under the circumstances, prior to marriage, it is only natural for the Catholic individual of the partnership to be unstinting in praise of the character, personality, and integrity of the non-Catholic individual. This is natural. As Bacon says, they're speaking ". . . in a perpetual hyperbole that is common in nothing but love." But the facts are that the promises are usually not kept, and the biggest problems discovered in mixed marriages are always on the matter of religion and religious beliefs, divorce, birth control, and the religious upbringing of children.

The following subjects are aspects of what is generally referred to as the essence of the marriage contract: the indissolubility of that contract, the purpose of that contract, the production of new life and the religious upbringing of the children who are the fruit of that contract. As arguments or problems arise concerning these subjects—which is the essence of a contract which has been freely entered into by people dedicated to the proposition that marriage is a holy means by which they may each more readily reach their salvation—one begins to see how readily the partners in a mixed marriage can become strangers in so many areas in which they should meet firmly on common ground. That is why marriage counselors and authorities on the subject of marriage, people who meet couples with problems, are entitled to raise an attitude of healthy skepticism on the compelling issue of how well do the couple know each other prior to marriage.

In mixed marriages particularly, people are made aware of the fact that when you marry an individual you *do* marry their family, surroundings, culture, racial traditions, national prejudices, and customs, to say nothing of family memories. Particularly difficult is the situation in which the woman is the non-Catholic and is a strong-minded individual. Since the woman "brings up" the children in our society to a much greater degree than the husband does—that is, the nature of our living is such that the children are generally with their mother pretty close to twenty-four hours a day, whereas the father is limited in the hours in which he may spend with his children—the religious training becomes largely a function of the mother; and the difficulty involved with the mixed marriage in this situation is that the mother under these conditions may simply elect to do nothing about it. Faith, though a precious gift of God, must be fostered. Neglect of the children's religion under these circumstances must inevitably lead to lack of religious training on the part of the children. Stormy sessions on this subject between a strong-minded father and a strong-minded mother who can reach no effective compromise are a horrible example to children.

These are the important functions in marriage, and if the couple find themselves cut off from each other and strangers on these subjects, it takes little imagination to see the road that such a marriage must take.

Before we leave the subject of mixed marriages, it should be remembered that the partners in mixed marriages are generally less loyal to any faith than even lukewarm churchgoers who are not involved in mixed marriages. It is really no wonder, then, that all church groups are concerned over the apparent increase in mixed marriages.

In mixed marriages, we are reminded of the tremendous

importance of the mother, her influence on the child, its early upbringing, and its religion. Statistics on mixed marriages indicate that the female has greater religious fervor and a natural antipathy towards divorce.

It has been shown that the children tend to follow the religion of the mother in mixed marriages. In mixed marriages in which the mother is a non-Catholic, divorces are much higher than in those in which the mother is a Catholic. When the mother is a Catholic and the father a non-Catholic, the rate of divorce is approximately the same low level that is found when both parents are Catholic.

The Legal Problems of Marriage

Anyone who has any knowledge of human nature knows that people who enter into marriage get into difficulties just as people do who enter into a business or a profession. From what we have stated already, it is obvious that some unfortunate people get involved in invalid marriages (marriages which are not marriages at all) and illicit or illegal marriages. Sometimes a person enters into a perfectly legal, valid marriage with a person he loves only to find that time and the erosions of life affect a personality that was perhaps not stable in the beginning and change the partner to a dangerous person who, even in the absence of violence, can have a catastrophic effect on good family living, the proper rearing of children, and the proper pursuit of one's religion.

Persons who become married in the face of an impeding or prohibitory impediment (e.g., mixed religion) and wish their marriage "straightened out," may obtain a dispensation through the Chancery office and be absolved in confession.

If the marriage is invalid, it must be so on the basis of either lack of proper form, imperfect consent, or some existing diriment impediment.

1. If there has been improper form; that is, two people, neither married previously, have attempted marriage before a Justice of the Peace or a minister of another faith, they must be married in the presence of a priest and two witnesses. The matter can be settled by the bishop or the pastor after the usual investigation that takes place before any valid marriage.

2. If the invalidity is due to defective consent or imperfect consent (cf. pages 83-85), the matter is relatively simple. If the individual involved with the defective consent is properly instructed as to what consent means, and there are no other obstacles, the consent may be rectified and the marriage thereby validated.

3. If the marriage is invalid by reason of a diriment impediment from which the Church customarily dispenses —for example, the impediment of relationship by blood or marriage—a dispensation may be obtained from the Bishop of the Diocese through the Chancery office and the marriage validated.

If the marriage *cannot* be made valid—for example, there is a pre-existing valid marriage—then the couple are not man and wife and must cease living together as such. If they wish to separate, subsequent action depends upon the cause of the invalidity.

If the invalidity is due to the existing bond of a previous marriage, the solemn vow on the part of one, holy orders, disparity of worship (that is, with a person who is not baptized), blood relationship (e.g., first cousins), affinity (e.g., a brother-in-law or sister-in-law after the death of the spouse), or spiritual relationship (the spiritual bond between the person who did the baptizing and the baptized, or the God-parent and the baptized) and it is clear from documents stemming from competent authority that the impediment exists and that further it cannot be dispensed—no judicial trial is necessary at the marriage court; the Bishop of the Diocese can declare the attempted union in marriage null and void.

All other cases of "invalid marriages" must be presented to a diocesan marriage court consisting of three judges. If the decision of such a court is that the marriage is invalid, the case must always be appealed to a superior court. If the diocesan court finds the marriage to be valid, unless the plaintiff wishes to appeal, the matter is closed. In any case, whether the marriage is declared null and void or valid, if both courts give the same decision the matter is considered closed, unless new evidence is presented. If the decision of the two courts differ, the case may then be referred to the Rota in Rome and tried again.

Earlier we mentioned the unhappy people who find that either they did not marry the personality they thought they did or things have changed so as to make living with their partner an unwholesome, dangerous, or catastrophic affair. These people generally look to the Church for some relief.

Some of them are sufficiently naive to feel that they can reach a divorce. From what has been said up to now, divorce from a valid marriage is obviously impossible. Two people baptized, giving free consent, enter into a contract by which they swear each other in marriage until the death of one of the parties. This contract results in a relationship in which the link that binds them is God Himself. As the ministers of their sacrament, of their contract, they are the means by which grace flows from God one to the other, and this is a bond that they have entered into as a means of helping each other on the way back to God. This being so, there is no one on earth who can remove God from their midst. The sacred nature of the bond, of the valid contract, between two married people makes divorce impossible.

Not uncommonly, those who find themselves in marital difficulties and realize that divorce is impossible turn to a maneuver which is generally referred to in common parlance as seeing if "the marriage can be dissolved." Actually, there are two situations under which a valid marriage can be dissolved. Technically, this is referred to as the dissolution of the bond.

The first of these is the non-consummated marriage. A non-consummated, valid marriage can be dissolved by the Pope himself on proof of two grounds: One, that there is a just cause and two, that no sexual intercourse has taken place and the marriage is therefore non-consummated.

Some just causes are: probable impotence on the part of one with the danger of incontinence on the part of the other; a civil divorce obtained by one party and the danger of incontinence on the part of the other; the danger of grave scandal; or serious reason for believing that the marriage was invalid for want of consent or because of some diriment impediment.

As for the non-consummation of the marriage, the Church seeks proof of this beyond reasonable doubt. In general, it is almost impossible to prove that the marriage is non-consummated, and if a bride and groom have spent their wedding night together, the assumption is that the marriage has been consummated until proven otherwise.

The second rare condition under which the bond of marriage may be dissolved is what is usually referred to as The Pauline Privilege because it originates from the teaching of

St. Paul to the Corinthians. It pertains to a legitimate marriage between non-baptized persons even though the marriage may have been consummated. St. Paul taught that if one member of such a marriage was converted and the unbaptized spouse was not converted but continued to live in a normal, married, happy state at peace with the other one, there is no problem. "But if the unbeliever depart, let him depart. For a brother or sister is not under servitude in such cases." (I Cor. 7:15.)

There are certain conditions associated with what is known as The Pauline Privilege. These are:

1. The original union in legitimate marriage must have been between two people who were at that time unbaptized.
2. Subsequent to the marriage one of the parties must have been converted to the Catholic faith.
3. The non-converted party refuses to live peacefully as man or wife. (This fact must be established by documentary proof in order for the privilege to be granted.)
4. The member who has been converted to the Catholic faith contracts a new marriage with another Catholic individual.

At the moment of the new marriage the old one is dissolved. The aggrieved partner in a difficult marriage who realizes that divorce is impossible, and that neither The Pauline Privilege nor the dissolution of a non-consummated marriage is applicable, usually seeks a separation. The Church recognizes certain circumstances under which it is no longer wise nor safe for the partners to live together as man and wife. Separation, however, is not made easy. It cannot be made easy because two people validly married and entering into a marriage with full consent, agree to marry for better, for worse, for richer, for poorer, in sickness and in health, until death. Their obligation is to live with one another as man and wife and to share and solve their problems as well as their joys until death. The Church recognizes, however, that separation is preferable under some conditions. Therefore, separation of two people in marriage is sometimes permitted.

Permanent separation is permitted under only two conditions. If both partners wish to enter a religious life, then by mutual consent they may be given permission to separate. The second situation in which permanent separation is permitted is adultery on the part of one member.

Temporary separation by mutual consent, agreement of husband and wife, may be justified by circumstances. The deterring factors which should make a husband and wife hesitate for a long period of time before making such a decision on their own are: first, by their vows they are obliged to live together; secondly, there is the danger of scandal; and third, there is the occasion of sin.

If the problem is one of a serious nature, and if it is probable that the separation may last any period of time, the couple should seek their pastor, who may in turn seek clarification from the Bishop. According to Canon 1131, one party may separate from the other without mutual consent if: (1) the other party falls away from the Church and joins a non-Catholic religion; (2) if that same party insists on giving the children a non-Catholic education; (3) if the party leads a criminal or disgraceful life; (4) if that party causes serious danger to the soul or body of the other; (5) if one party by cruelty makes life together too difficult; or (6) similar causes.

It is important to realize that the Bishop has jurisdiction over such separation. He must be consulted, and he must give his authorization. In an emergency, where there is danger from physical harm, the couple may separate; otherwise, the case should be brought before the Bishop of the

Diocese. Separation is never permitted for trivial reasons—for instance, the incompatibilities which assault us from the tabloid newspapers every day. And one essential feature of temporary separation is that once the compelling reason which has authorized the separation has disappeared the couple is required to live together as man and wife.

6

Premarital Examination
and Conferences

The premarital examination consists of a medical and social history of the patient and a complete physical examination. As a result of these findings, there follows a discussion of any immediate personal problems, and a general discussion of problems pertaining to marriage. It is, of course, an ideal opportunity to raise questions involving sex, reproduction, pregnancy, and family limitation. Most marriage counselors consider the premarital examination to be extremely valuable; many feel it is imperative.

Obviously, the premarital examination is complete only if both partners take it. This applies particularly to the discussion phase. Discussion of subjects pertaining to marriage and sex should probably be done by the same person or persons for both the future husband and wife. Indeed, by offering a common forum for such talks for both the fellow and the girl, the Pre-Cana Conferences have done heroic work along these lines. Premarital courses and premarital lectures have been, wisely or not, pretty much restricted to colleges and premarital examinations have been largely confined to people with specific concern or some actual problem prior to marriage. (Happily, individual premarital conferences and examinations are somewhat on the increase.) Often the greatest amount of assistance to the greatest number of people comes from the Pre-Cana Conference. These conferences are generally held from four to six weeks (occasionally, in some areas, they last longer) for engaged couples. In most areas with which I have been associated, the prior requirement has been that the couple be engaged and have set a date for their marriage. This, I am sure, varies to some extent throughout the country. In some parishes, also, great emphasis is placed upon the desirability of a couple bringing a certificate from a Pre-Cana Conference when they come to the rectory to discuss the details of arrangements for the marriage itself.

Pre-Cana Conferences consist of a series of group discussions on marriage as a contract and vocation, its spiritual values, its physical facts, and its social and economic aspects. These conferences are generally in the care of a priest, who lectures about marriage as a contract, a sacrament, and a vocation, emphasizing the spiritual and emotional aspects of common life together. A physician or physicians are generally asked to lecture on the physical aspects of love and living together, some of the problems of early pregnancy, matters of emotional and mental importance, and health. A married couple is frequently asked to talk—either as members of a panel or in an individual session—about marriage as a living institution and the problems that are found in marriage itself. In varying communities, a lawyer, a social worker, someone from public health units, and someone who has specific information on budgeting and economics are asked to give short talks or to appear on panels to answer questions from the engaged couples.

There are still people with the peculiar idea that Pre-Cana Conferences are sex-teaching sessions—how to make love by the numbers; the Church's teaching on sex, etc. Actually their purpose is to develop and strengthen attitudes on marriage, and certain information must be given to properly fulfill this service. Too many people enter marriage who have little or no idea of the nature of its solemn, binding contract. The word "contract" has more real reference to baseball than to marriage; the word "binding" unhappily has come to mean that a high-priced lawyer is needed to break it.

It is not uncommon at a Pre-Cana Conference to see at least a few who are shaken by what they are told by the priest, doctor, or married couple. Girls who (almost literally) have no idea of their own biological function, sometimes accompany fellows who have almost no concept of their obligations as lovers and husbands. There are still some girls who have been warned (by their mothers?) of the predatory nature of the male and the role in life of the poor, suffering female. Not at all unknown either, is the male who is looking for another mother—a contemporary companion and nurse.

I firmly believe that these conferences should be attended by all engaged couples—there is certainly something of value in them for every engaged person. Many couples must be aroused from a naive and sentimental state to the certain knowledge that to make marriage successful they've got to work at it; that marriage is a road back to God and however difficult the road, it must be traveled until death. One doesn't make such a journey with a "nice boy" or a "sweet girl"; this kind of travel requires a real man and a real woman genuinely mated in love, striding at a hiker's pace, secure in their love and their appointment with God. In the highly impressionable period of engagement, with the marriage date usually set, the Pre-Cana Conferences should say in effect: If this is the kind of marriage you are entering—Go with God and with His speed. On the other hand, if your contemplated marriage doesn't measure up—then make haste slowly, think it over; postpone; view the field.

The decision to marry is not usually difficult. The decision whom you will marry is important. The happiness and possibly the salvation of two people are at stake, as are the lives and happiness of unborn children.

Pre-Cana Conferences have a value for all engaged couples. Anything that with good taste can further impress the couple with the serious and enduring nature of marriage has ample justification in modern life; in fact, it is a firm conviction of many that the solemn engagement should in some way be linked with this movement.

The Pre-Cana Conferences, of course, have their limitations. From a physician's point of view, a doctor's talk on the physical aspect of marriage in the Pre-Cana Conference is impossible—the lecturer is trying to discuss a personal subject to a group. Paradoxically, therein lies one of the great values of the Pre-Cana Conference—not only does the lecturer realize that the subject can be adequately treated only at a personal level but so do many in the audience. Many couples that could never seek a premarital examination are urged to do so by the attitude and sense of responsible inquiry supplied them by the Pre-Cana Conferences.

Reasons for Premarital Examination

1. As already indicated, one reason to have a premarital examination is to have a frank discussion of sex, family limitation, and marriage problems together.
2. It is a good way for a couple to start doing important things together. For many couples the premarital examination seems like a drastic or unusual step, particularly if

neither person has seen a physician for several years. There is, of course, always a certain amount of apprehension that the physician will find in one or both some strange or unsuspected illness. This rarely happens. In any case, when a couple agrees to a physical examination, one more barrier or fear is broken down and the important problem of health is put into proper perspective.

3. It enables a couple to raise questions concerning health and illness, physical and emotional, which may then be answered in an authoritative way in the beginning of a marriage.

4. If either partner has any illness such as an ulcer, a residual from an old polio, epilepsy, etc., it gives both an opportunity to get an appraisal of such a problem in relation to their life together.

5. It gives a couple the chance to learn about hereditary and familial illnesses and congenital defects, which are problems in the minds of most couples. These problems are not well understood by medical authorities, and most people outside of medicine lack even their proper definitions. Confusion, therefore, lends panic to worry and many people are disturbed unnecessarily.

The term "heredity" refers to the direct line of inheritance—grandparents, parents, and children. The term "familial" refers to brothers, sisters, and cousins. By congenital, we mean a condition which is present when a child is born and which obviously developed during the fetal life. This condition may be due in part to heredity, that is, based upon some characteristic from either parent; or it may be environmental—due to some change in the nourishment of the child in utero or to some toxic product or infection to which the mother was exposed during the pregnancy. The list of such possibilities is interminable. Most people trust to luck or to the kindness of the Lord that such things will not be visited upon them. However, if there is a problem to be found within the family of one prospective mate, and it is causing anxiety, the premarital examination and the interview associated with it, can help to assuage the couple's fears and worries. Not infrequently, young people, as marriage approaches, become increasingly aware of marriage problems and the children around them. Inevitably, some of them see retarded or abnormal children. Inevitably, the learned relative or "family expert" spreads his or her misinformation—and the young people become confused and anxious.

Thus, the knowledge that the chance against any pregnancy ending in a serious congenital defect or serious developmental abnormality is about forty to one can give great solace to such people. Similarly, any family in which a female member has developed breast cancer before the age of thirty-five should be apprized of the fact that the disease is a familial one especially in such an instance. It should be made clear that when cancer of the breast occurs in any woman under thirty-five, all of her sisters should be examined at frequent intervals for possible detection of a tumor, and that all of these sisters should be taught to examine their own breasts for their own protection.

Diabetes, of course, is hereditary, and when we remember that one person in three in the United States has a predisposition to diabetes, we realize that the disease is fairly common. The estimate of whose children and how many will have diabetes varies tremendously depending upon the diabetic history on one side of the family, the other side, or both. The essence of this whole discussion concerning congenital, hereditary, and familial problems in the premarital interview is that the truth does set people free, or it at least gives them the maturity to be able to accept what they cannot change. Somewhere it has been said that those who have learned to accept what they cannot change in life have taken the first step to happiness. From the doctor's point of view, this particular phase of the premarital examination and interview is important because it gives him an opportunity to scotch so many old wives' tales.

6. The premarital examination gives the prospective mates (sometimes for the first time) an opportunity as adults to talk to a physician about important, adult responsibilities. Most people's concept of a physician is apt to be carried over from childhood; a premarital examination helps to erase the bogey-man image and the fear associated with it. At the same time it builds up the attitude that a physician's function is to help, to educate (however painful may be the process), and to serve as a friend.

One of the secondary benefits that may derive from the premarital examination is the physician's success in putting across the importance of the annual check-up. This program tends to invite the sly comment that the doctor is trying to build up business for the profession, but it is becoming apparent, I think, to the American public, that an annual examination is assuming more and more importance all the time. So far as the male is concerned, it is the only brake that can be placed upon such problems as excess weight, beginning high blood pressure, heart disease, kidney disease, ulcers, and other serious illnesses which seem to be common among men. So far as the female is concerned, among the various conditions which may be picked up early by annual check-ups are two which are outstanding:

The first of these is cancer of the breast. Cancer of the breast is the primary cause of death from cancer in the American woman. It is a very unhappy disease which tends to occur in women at a time when their families need them the most—when their children are finishing their education, entering new careers, starting families of their own. As a matter of fact, it strikes women at a time when they can enjoy their own families the most and spoil their grandchildren on the side. Cancer of the breast rarely strikes without warning. The disease is usually discovered by the patient herself. Unfortunately, many women, when they notice a lump, instead of consulting a physician immediately, all too commonly conceal both their fear and the lump until it is too late. It is possible, under modern conditions of examination, to detect at annual check-ups breast conditions at a very early age, to discover malignancies when they are early and treatable, and to remove benign but tumorous conditions which might eventually lead to something more serious.

The second condition involves the womb in particular and the reproductive organs in general. Tumors of the reproductive system in the female are ten times more common than they are in the male. It is, therefore, a very important subject for a woman to know something about. Even if she knows little or nothing about tumors, if she realizes that an annual check-up can insure her safety against the diseases of the reproductive organs, then she will have accomplished much towards her own safety and towards the happiness of her family.

1. The most common tumor of the womb is called fibroid. This is a hard, fleshy, benign tumor of the womb which can grow rapidly, induce pain, and cause serious bleeding in any woman, and particularly in the woman approaching menopause. It has been said that a womb that isn't busy making babies is busy making fibroids. Therefore, fibroids are frequently found in single women,

and usually their symptoms are dramatic in the sense of pain or hemorrhage. Occasionally, however, there are no symptoms with them and only the annual check-up will uncover them.

2. Cancer of the body of the womb is not an uncommon disease, and it is found in women at or slightly beyond the change of life. The usual symptom is the development of a discharge or irregular or peculiar bleeding. It is notoriously a slowly growing cancer, and *when detected at an early stage,* especially as a result of the annual check-up (and hopefully before symptoms have occurred), a doctor can almost guarantee to a woman that she may die of old age rather than of cancer of the body of the womb.

3. Cancer of the neck of the womb (the cervix) is known as the "cancer of neglect." It is almost never found in a cervix that is clean, smooth, and healthy. The best insurance that we have against the development of cancer of the neck of the womb is to have the cervix examined every year and treat it whenever minor disease develops in it. In other words, the best insurance against cancer of the neck of the womb is to keep it clean and healthy. Of particular importance in this regard is the visit that is paid to the physician after the delivery of a baby. There are often erosions or raw areas in the cervix, or small cracks or minor infections, all of which can be treated simply in the office.

It is perhaps well to add in this regard, that it is possible to diagnose any disease of the cervix as an office procedure. It is, furthermore, possible to treat the vast majority of cases of diseases of the cervix in the office. The problem is always to persuade the patients to come back year after year, especially after the age of thirty, to have the cervix examined. Whenever a woman has a discharge which is "different," irritating, itchy, or colored (yellow, brown, green, etc.), it should be investigated because it generally indicates that there is infection, inflammation, or some (usually minor) problem in the neck of the womb which needs correction.

4. Tumors of the Fallopian tube are quite rare, but other diseases of the tube, particularly infections, are not at all uncommon. Again the diagnosis of most diseases of the tube is an office procedure, but the treatment may require hospitalization or even surgery.

5. Tumors of the vagina are quite rare. They are easily diagnosed as an office procedure, but they can be treated successfully only if detected early. The most common problem associated with the vagina is an infection or inflammation which is again diagnosed in the office and can be treated simply as an office procedure.

6. Tumors of the ovary are all treacherous and *must* be diagnosed early. Hence, the value of the annual check-up after thirty. There are many types of tumors of the ovary, and they are not at all uncommon. Most ovarian cysts are benign, and some of the solid tumors are benign. But because tumors of the ovary which are malignant tend to spread rapidly, every woman, especially as she gets older, should be examined by a physician at least once a year.

7. Tumors of the vulvae or lips of the vagina are generally associated with considerable itching, scratching, and pain. They are usually found in older women, but occasionally we find them as early as the third decade of life. Most of the conditions of the vulvae are benign, and it is rather uncommon to find tumors. But again, early detection is important for the cure of tumors of the vulvae.

8. The development of the Papanicoloau smear or "screening smear," as it is known, has made possible the detection of tumors in the reproductive tract of women long
before they are detectable by the naked eye or can be
palpated by the examining finger. It is important to
remember, however, that the woman who does not have
an annual check-up is denying herself the benefit of this
test.

Factual information for the engaged couple about life and
love is necessary, particularly if it is candid and sincere,
offers something new, and is perhaps glamorized by the
presence and words of a physician. But information is merely
the frosting on the cake. The cake itself must be the attitude
which the two people bring to marriage.

Selecting a Physician

The selection of a physician is a cause of great concern for
many newly-weds. As a matter of fact, it is a common question in Pre-Cana Conferences. Not infrequently, a doctor in
his office is suddenly confronted by a patient whom he has
known for many years and who is now moving to another
section of the country and wants to know how to find a
doctor. Questions about and criticisms of doctors not only
are legion, they are popular press, popular politics, and
popular humor. Nevertheless, to the individual, the physician
is important—not only as a friend in need but as a friend.

The question often comes up of whether or not to go to a
Catholic doctor. The term "Catholic doctor" implies that
there is a separate breed of doctor who is characteristically
Catholic and, therefore, is a characteristic type of physician.
But in a very real sense, there is no such thing as a Catholic

doctor. There are not a few Catholics who also happen to be physicians and surgeons; there are some physicians and surgeons who are Catholics.

The doctor who is a Catholic does not feel himself to be under a cloud thereby, nor does he feel inadequate in any phase of medicine, nor penalized because of his religion, nor limited in any way in bringing the most scientific solutions to his patient's problems. As a Catholic, he is required to do neither more nor less than any good Catholic is required to do, and as a physician he can and does bring the same scientific attitude, precision, and good judgment to his patient that any non-Catholic physician does.

There are moral principles which must guide the actions of every man, including the physician. There is a standard of morality which is not relative nor changeable according to the caprice of individuals or the era in which it is applied. The Catholic physician is convinced that inasmuch as God is the author of good morality and good medicine he cannot, by definition, be contradictory and that, therefore, a scientific answer must and can be found within the confines of good morality in any particular instance. There is no implication here that the discovery of such an answer or the answer itself will be easy or the implementation of it simple. The precise meaning is that no moral standard can be transgressed on the ground of expediency. Many of the medico-moral problems, as they are known, occur in obstetrics because of the nature of maternity work, the fact that there are two patients, and because of the dramatic and emotional components of the birth process. Abortion is a case in point. For years, when others insisted that abortion was the only solution to a difficult problem in maternity work, the Catholic physician steadfastly maintained it could not be done because it represented the murder of the unborn child and that, furthermore, it was not necessary for the successful solution in the pregnancy. I think that there are very few people today, Catholic or non-Catholic, who insist upon the necessity of abortion as an answer to any medical problem in obstetrics. We agree that the management, for example, of a pregnant woman with a bad heart may be somewhat expensive, tedious, worrisome, and difficult, but there is little question from a review of the medical literature that any such problem cannot be successfully solved without interruption of the pregnancy. As a matter of fact, within the past few years, one of our distinguished non-Catholic obstetricians has stated that wherever there appears to be a serious indication for abortion, therein lies its greatest single contraindication.

As to whether or not the Catholic patient should seek a Catholic physician, the answer is simple and obvious:

1. The most precious bond and most important feature in the relationship between patient and doctor is the faith which the patient has in the doctor's interest in him and in his ability to help. Most non-Catholic doctors are very much aware of those phases of medicine which involve a moral standard to which the Catholic is particularly attuned. Most non-Catholic physicians respect the convictions of their Catholic patients and are careful to guard the Catholic's conscience in such instances; frequently, they either consult a Catholic colleague or insist that the patient consult a priest before any recommended course of action be taken.

2. No non-Catholic physician in my acquaintance becomes disturbed or incensed or upset if, in a given situation, consultation with a priest or consultation with a Catholic doctor is requested.

3. Occasionally, a patient may want to consult with a

Catholic doctor to discuss some problem from a purely Catholic point of view, for example, the point of view of Catholic philosophy or morals. The non-Catholic physician usually does not know enough about Church teaching to be able to assess competently the patient's problem or give the proper depth of reassurance. In such cases, the Catholic physician can serve readily as a consultant without interfering with the proper patient-doctor relationship.

Being a Catholic doesn't "qualify" a doctor—it emphasizes his philosophy and the standards by which he professes to live. It simply demonstrates again that a professional and scientific person can live and practice his profession and his religion in the certain knowledge that the Same One "wrote the book" for both.

As stated above, the one most abiding important feature in the relationship between the doctor and the patient is faith. The physician who, regardless of his training, has developed within the patient a faith in his interest in him or her can do far more than a learned professor who is twenty years ahead of his time in knowledge, diagnosis, and treatment, but is so preoccupied in his cases that the patient has no faith in him. And faith is such a warm, comfortable, and personal thing that it is not so surprising that it is rather seldom broken. The doctor who is aware of his patient's faith in him is flattered by it, but he is also made humble by it, for this faith is something that frightens every doctor at the beginning of his day.

Competence in a physician we tend to take for granted. In this country there are now relatively few sources of incompetently trained physicians. Competence is desirable and necessary, but as indicated above, interest is frequently more essential than brilliance.

There is much to be said these days about the general practitioner, or the G.P. as he is known, and how he is vanishing from the scene. A better term, perhaps, is the family doctor. He has been with us for a long time, and although his credentials are somewhat different, he is still with us today. The general practice of medicine, certainly within the larger cities, is disappearing. The reason does not seem to be because specialists are freezing general practitioners out of work. The plain fact is that the horizons of medicine have so broadened in the last fifty years that it is almost impossible for any man these days to have a "general knowledge" of medicine. In the large cities where there tend to be more specialists, opportunities for seeing doctors who have a specialized knowledge of a certain problem are available to the community; there is, therefore, in addition, a much less greater need for a general man. Nor do people use the term general practitioner in the hallowed sense of the family friend who was the family doctor years ago. The general practitioner today is usually seen as a man who can answer his phone and subsequently visit the home—on what very well may be an unnecessary call.

Rapid means of transportation and the widespread dissemination of health information, have made it possible to solve more and more problems over the telephone. It is difficult to estimate accurately, but it is assumed that at least 40 per cent of emergencies, especially those that occur at night, are emergencies only because they happen at night, drugstores are closed, and the patient and his or her family have been neglecting the symptoms for two or three days. The man who is really challenged to be a practitioner of the general knowledge of medicine is the physician who practices general medicine in outlying suburbia where there are no immediate sources of specialized information and where he must carry the ball himself. The herculean task which he has set for himself, the dedication which motivates it, and the heroics which he performs every day can only partially be demonstrated by the fact that modern medicine in the content of knowledge required is revising itself, renewing itself, or doubling itself every five years.

Who then is becoming the family doctor of modern medicine? There has been no intention on the part of any group to usurp the function of the family doctor as such, but it seems that the internist is becoming the family doctor for men and the obstetrician-gynecologist for women. These are the doctors who get to know their patients most thoroughly, each in his respective field. And so, in addition to taking care of the usual problems of medicine in their own fields, they have become the referring doctors to other specialists when the need arises.

What, then, is the answer to the question, whom shall you select for your physician? The ideal answer is to get a family doctor. Whether he be a general practitioner or a specialist in any field is rather unimportant; the idea is to have a doctor in whom you have faith and who can be a friend to you. In any medical problem, when should a patient be satisfied with a general practitioner and when with a specialist? This question as it is posed to us many times is rather snobbish in its nature. It is not a question of being satisfied with a general practitioner. The question here is having faith in the competence of the doctor. The general practitioner, the general man—as he is sometimes called—the G.P., the family doctor, the medical friend that you have down the block is going to be the first one to call for help when and if it is needed. There are many rather simple problems in all phases of medicine which a competent general practitioner can manage very successfully. The family doctor in whom you have faith will not let you down.

If a couple or an individual is in a strange community and is looking for a physician, whether it be for a general man or for a specialist, there are numerous sources of information.

The first is the State Medical Society or the Local County Medical Society. In some areas there is even a Municipal Medical Society. All such groups will be happy to furnish you with a list of competent, accredited men in a general or specific field.

The AMA Directory is found in all public libraries. It lists every accredited physician in this country, and if the symbols are properly evaluated, it is possible to determine what is the man's primary field of interest and his specialty.

If a specialist is sought, again, in a public library there is a directory of Medical Specialists in which are listed, by their specialty, and by city and state, all of the accredited specialists who have chosen to take the specialist's examinations set up by the profession for recognition in a particular field. The fact that a man appears in such a volume indicates essentially that he has been trained in a particular field and to what degree he has been trained. There are many competent men within a given specialty who have had competent training but who, for personal reasons, prefer not to take the examinations and so are not listed in such a directory. In this case, such men will almost always appear on a list of doctors given on application by any local hospital. Finally, friends, neighbors, and clergy will personally evaluate a physician, as a professional and as an individual. Many times an appraisal of a physician as an individual will be different from yours. This is simply human nature. Occasionally, an evaluation of the physician's competence may be completely wrong. This, again, is the human equation. All of these are careful adjuncts, and many of them have been successfully used. It is probable, however, that the referral by a family doctor to another doctor when a specialist is needed is the best source.

Here are a few words of advice that perhaps should be offered at this time. These are not necessarily any group of doctors' pet peeves, but they are features of physician-patient relationships which are important for the comfort and care of the patient:

1. Try to call a physician early in the day if possible, if the problem seems at all urgent.
2. At least telephone before the druggist in the local community closes.
3. Remember that many problems can be handled, at least on an emergency basis, by telephone. Some problems have a characteristic story. Other matters are obvious to the physician who is familiar with the type of infections prevalent in the community.
4. Don't take anyone else's prescriptions no matter how good they seem to have been for the other fellow.
5. Follow directions given for prescriptions. If a doctor writes for ten days' medication, it is because it has been found that if the medication is not taken for at least ten days the patient's illness will return, sometimes with renewed vigor.
6. The pediatrician or any physician handling children and newborns must be guided by certain practical rules governing infection. Patients frequently become upset because the physician is "late" in making a call; they do not realize that, except in an emergency, he has an obligation not to go from a patient who is infectious (e.g., strep) to a newborn nursery or clean surgical patient.
7. If your doctor is strict, be grateful. Physicians have to be

strong-minded because they cannot afford to be care-less. Any physician who is strict is assuming his proper role.

Every physician, as he practices the healing art, plays several roles. He is expected to be a scientist but not in the sense of the mathematician; he is expected to be a friend, a father confessor, a defender of hope, and a bulwark to morale. He is also expected to be a Dutch uncle and an educator—but these are not his popular roles. There are times when the physician must be serious and stern—when the patient does not cooperate or takes contrary advice from a non-medical source, or fails to get the prescribed medication, or take it as directed.

When the physician functions as an educator, his role is most difficult. To the obese patient who is in trouble because of the obesity, he must point out that only the patient can diet and, essentially, only dieting is the answer. A "nervous" or "tense" patient must be told that medication can be of assistance in making him feel better temporarily but, too frequently, such a patient must be told that his symptoms will disappear only when he (or she) faces up to the cause of the tension or learns to accept it.

The biggest challenge in medicine is always the patient who (usually not deliberately) doesn't let the physician help him; he or she must be educated to do so. Families can render material assistance here by conferring with the physician, by keeping him up to date, and by support and encouragement of the patient.

In summary, you want a physician who is competent; you need a physician who can also be a friend. In any case, to be successful with you, the physician must have your faith, and you must have respect for his judgment. The physician's interest is almost paramount; it is to a large extent a measure of his love for his fellow man. But whoever the physician, or whatever may be his talents, remember he cannot do the job alone. He must have your help.

7

The Marriage
and the Honeymoon

It is time now for us to turn to a consideration of the wedding day itself, the nature of the decisions which have to be made concerning it, the honeymoon which follows, and some comments on the early days of marriage.

Marriage is a happy step in life but solemn, too, and must be taken seriously. It is a transitional period during which the couple enters a new state of social living. Almost automatically a couple on the threshold of marriage make an examination of conscience. They become concerned about their past misdeeds, and during the period of the engagement especially, conversation gets very personal. This is particularly true just before marriage. At such times, some people have an almost scrupulous attitude about revealing things to their future partner in marriage. In this respect, Father Edward Healy in his *Marriage Guidance* says that there are three things to be considered:

1. The individual must reveal whatever would make the marriage injurious to the other party such as serious disease, public disgrace, moral defects, large debts, or sterility produced by an operation.

2. The individual may or may not reveal defects that make marriage less desirable but not intolerable; bodily deformity, low birth, poverty, a sharp disposition, or economic incompetence.

3. A person should not reveal failings of his or her past life, even serious ones, which are of no concern to the prospective mate. Such things are best left unsaid since they might ruin the chances of marriage or be brought up after marriage in arguments. This is based upon the ethical principle that a person is entitled to his or her own secrets. Inasmuch as marriage is a union peculiarly personal and intimate it requires that some secrets, for the good of the marriage, be known. It is equally obvious, however, that the ethical principle still holds in those aspects of those questions which are not germane to the marriage itself.

In most cases, a wedding represents the first major social event for which the bride plans all the details. She should derive a lesson from it—to learn to plan so that every major event in her life as a married woman will be well thought out in advance. This point is sometimes difficult to get across to the bride.

As soon as a decision has been reached by the couple to marry, they should set their wedding date with as little delay as possible, regardless of how far off that date may be. There are many reasons for deciding upon the date months ahead of the actual ceremony itself. Personal reasons may motivate the selection of a particular day or date; it may be set for the day upon which someone dear was married, or on an anniversary of the day the couple first met, or on a day which will conveniently fit in with the plans for the wedding trip. Sometimes, when the couple's passions are beginning to be aroused too quickly and too deeply, they agree to move the wedding date forward. Another common personal reason for setting a specific date is the expected date of a girl's menstrual period since most brides would rather have just completed a period on the day of their wedding.

Then again, in parishes with a large family-type congregation (as opposed to a retired one) there may be many weddings scheduled on particular days in certain months, and if a girl waits too long, she may find it impossible to arrange her wedding for the date she desires. Planning her wedding well in advance, then, is a good object lesson for a bride to learn so future events can be carried off with efficiency and dispatch.

The Wedding

An important consideration of any wedding is the cost. It will depend upon two major factors—whether the wedding will be formal or simple and the number of guests. A formal wedding requires many more attendants, which, of course, entails greater expense. Since wedding expenses may easily run into thousands of dollars, the bride should discuss them very frankly with both her groom-to-be and her family (who, after all, usually pay the bills). They should determine whether or not a large wedding is what the couple really wants or whether, beyond a certain amount, the money would be more profitably used in setting up a home and establishing credit to make the first few years of marriage more smooth. No one can really make this decision except the bride, but some consideration, unfortunately, sometimes must be given to the social status of the family in selecting the date and the size and type of wedding. However, if a bride carefully uses good taste, she can without offense to anyone circumvent any awkward problems.

The season of the year for which a wedding is scheduled has some practical importance, particularly for Catholics. Weddings cannot be solemnized during Advent and Lent. The bride may also use the seasonal element to fashion the wedding to conform to her wishes. A change of only a week during the summer season may make the difference in the necessity for a formal or a simple wedding and, because of vacation plans involved, make the difference between a crowd of 300 or 100 in attendance.

There are many customs associated with the wedding ceremony, and most of them have interesting histories. The wedding ring, for example, is supposedly a duplicate of the betrothal ring. However, there are conflicting stories. The ring given in marriage (sometimes called the *amulet pronubis*) originally was worn supposedly as an amulet for protection against evil spirits, witches, and souls of the dead and as a life-giving symbol. It was a royal ornament symbolizing the marriage of a monarch to his kingdom just as the Episcopal ring represented the marriage of a Bishop to his See. In the wedding ceremony, it was associated with the *arrhae* given in the *sponsalis* as a pledge of the contract. By the time of Clement of Alexandria it was regarded as the seal upon the husband's goods, upon which the care and safekeeping of the house was centered. Later it became a sign of constancy and mutual trust, a seal of faith, and a symbol of the vow made between the couple.

The circle or ring signified eternity among the Egyptians, making it the ideal symbol for the eternal union between man and woman in an indissoluble marriage. The Egyptians also thought there was a vein, the vein of love, which went from the heart to the third finger of the left hand; that is why the wedding ring is placed on this finger. Macrobius, a Roman scholar of the fifth century A.D., said that the ring was placed on the finger to prevent the sentiments of the heart from escaping; that it was a permanent token of a woman's love for the man who placed it there. This is supposed to be the origin of the sentiment that under no circumstances was a woman to remove her wedding ring lest her love go with it.

The Jews placed the ring on the index finger of the right hand and among the Anglo-Saxons the ring was placed on the right hand until the wedding, when it was changed to the left hand. This is still done in some parts of middle Europe today.

Other reasons for the use of the left hand are found in the fact that the right hand was considered the hand of power and authority; the left, the hand of subordination. Therefore, the ring on the left hand of the wife meant that she was subordinate to the head of the household. Since the left hand in most people is used less than the right and the third finger of the left hand is used the least, the fact that the ring would get less wear and tear there may have had something to do with the choice.

The joining of hands at the wedding ceremony is symbolic of the sacramental union of husband and wife; this has its origin in the *dextrarum junctio* of the Romans which brought the bride under the hand (*manus*) of her husband. The gifts of something of gold to the bride are symbolic of the life-giving power with which gold was associated in primitive thinking. Originally, the bride and bridegroom were crowned with gold and silver or olive and myrtle. The crowns were a sign of victory over the forces of evil and death. In some of the Eastern rites, the bride and bridegroom are still crowned with jewels or olive and myrtle. But today, the veil usually takes the place of the crowning. The veil was originally a protection against the evil eye and other malign influences, but under Christian thinking became a symbol of constancy. Veils were also worn by widows who made a profession of continency. Later they became a part of the habit of nuns, from which the expression "taking the veil" originates. Indeed, in pagan Rome, the vestal virgins as sacred people had their heads covered with a hood, a *suffibulum,* during the performance of their sacrificial functions. The veil, therefore, both in pagan and Christian thinking, had a holy connotation, and originally was a means whereby holy people or objects were separated from the profane. Since the bride was in the process of passing into a new status in society, she required supernatural aid. At the time of Tertullian, the betrothal veil was worn by the bride from the day of her engagement until the day of her wedding to symbolize the unshakable fidelity—typified by the relationship between Christ and His Church—to which the wife was bound by virtue of the marriage contract. The veil, therefore, became a sign of consecration to the holiest state of marriage comparable to the solemn clothing of nuns in their positions as the spouses of Christ. Interestingly enough, in Roman life a red veil signified a married woman.

The wedding gown is a source of many superstitions and tales. It is a common belief that a white wedding gown signifies purity, innocence, and virginity, but this is not universal and not historically consistent. White was observed by the early Greeks as a sign of joy. The Greeks wore white clothing and white flowers on all feast days, and they painted their bodies white on the night before the wedding. Among the Chinese, however, white is used for mourning as a symbol of joy at the return of the deceased to his ancestors.

There are many interesting aspects to color. Black, for example, was first worn for mourning in ancient Rome. While in mourning, the women wore dresses called *lugubria* to express their sorrow at the loss of a loved one. However, under the Roman Emperors, white was worn instead. In the late fifteenth century, Anne of Brittany wore black for mourning at the death of her husband, Charles VIII, the first use of black for mourning since ancient Roman times.

Blue, a color symbolic of fair skies, signifies love everlasting. The expression "true blue" is still frequently used to express true love and friendship. The brides of Israel in ancient times wore a blue ribbon on the border of their gown to denote purity, fidelity, and love. It is said to have been assigned to the Royal House of David; today it is associated with the purity of the Blessed Virgin Mary.

Traditionally, white is the preference of most brides for formal weddings. When the ceremony is private, she may wear her own favorite color. Traditional wedding gowns among many people are made of a combination of a great many colors peculiar to the region of the country, and in many places there is a traditional costume, generally multicolored, to be worn by the bride only.

"Something old, something new, something borrowed, something blue" is a traditional marriage custom. The old article is generally a used article, such as a garter, which belongs to a happily married woman. It is symbolic of the older woman's happy married life, and the bride therefore wishes to attract some of her friend's good fortune to herself. The article must never come from a widow.

Everything about the bride is new and she is looking forward to her new life with great expectancy and high hopes. The selection of a handkerchief as the "something new" is apparently a matter of convenience—something to label and tuck away. It has no significance.

The "something borrowed" in ancient days was usually something precious and golden, usually a relative's jewel. It had to be made of gold to symbolize the sun, the source of life, the protector of the bride and all womanhood.

The "something blue" is usually some blue ribbon or a bead.

It is, again, symbolic of fair skies, signifying a love everlasting and the constancy of a true love. It also connotes purity and fidelity.

Orange blossoms traditionally have been carried by the bride. First of all, the orange tree is an evergreen and, therefore, is symbolic of the couple's everlasting love for one another. The orange tree bears blossoms and fruit at the same time; therefore, among the ancient Chinese the flowers are considered not only lucky but symbolic of the purity, chastity, and innocence of the bride, and because the blossoms and the fruit are always together these blossoms are symbolic of the fertility, hopefully, of the bride and worn as an emblem to insure against her barrenness. Among the ancients, brides carried bunches of herbs under their bridal veils or sheaves of wheat for the protection of fertility. The English have long favored roses as their bridal flowers and consequently there is some connection between roses and weddings in June, the month of roses.

The wedding commonly takes place in the parish of the bride. The pastor has the legal authority to perform it. He may delegate this authority to any of his curates or for a good reason delegate it to another priest—the bride's choice of a relative or dear friend. He may even, for good reason and on request of the bride, allow the marriage to take place at another parish. Arrangements for the wedding must be made by the couple with the pastor some weeks prior to the wedding because he is bound by Canon Law to talk to each member of the partnership privately to determine if they know the laws of the Church and if there is any impediment to the free consent which they are supposed to understand prior to the wedding. Secondly, the banns must be published. These require at least three weeks as a rule, since the banns must be published on three consecutive Sundays or Holy Days of Obligation. For good reason, the banns may be dispensed with, but ordinarily they are required except for mixed marriages, in which banns are never published—the Church is not anxious to publicize mixed marriages.

Time should be allotted wherever possible for marriage preparation courses, such as Pre-Cana Conferences, which are available either as diocesan or parish affairs, under study club auspices, or from the Family Life Bureau of the National Catholic Welfare Conference. All of these preparations require that a prudent person see the pastor to arrange for a marriage at least one and preferably two months before the marriage. Most marriage preparation courses require at least three weeks to fulfill, and while these may not be obligatory in any particular parish, their value, at least for some people, cannot be overestimated. If there are any complications involved in a particular marriage, it may take weeks, months, or even years to determine whether or not a marriage may be validly contracted. For example, notice must be obtained regarding the reception of Sacraments from every parish in which the members of the partnership have lived. The official arms of the Church in investigating marriage move slowly because they must be careful to protect marriage as a holy and sacred act. In the case of a mixed marriage, the non-Catholic party must take six instructions, the promises must be signed, and a dispensation sought from the Bishop. In most instances, this takes approximately one month.

The question who may be the attendants of the bride and groom at a wedding is frequently raised. The problem generally involved is that someone wants a non-Catholic as a member of the wedding party. The official witnesses to a wedding, since it is a sacrament, should be Roman Catholics. But for very good and sufficient reason the Bishop may grant a dispensation to allow, for example, a non-Catholic sister of the bride to be the maid of honor.

Music at a wedding is often a problem to the bride. She may

be sentimentally attached to certain songs or like the way a friend sings a particular song—and find that the songs which she has in mind are not allowed in her Church. Canon Law 1264 states in very general terms the type of music that is and is not permissible at a wedding. There is a serious obligation involved on the part of the pastor to be sure that improper music is eliminated from the Church. Some dioceses have lists of songs which are approved and banned. The local Church organist is generally well-acquainted with the music which is approved in the parish or diocese.

The presence of a photographer at a wedding is *de rigueur* for most brides. There are, however, regulations within parishes and dioceses specifying where the photographer may station himself, what type of pictures he may take, and at what parts of the Mass they may be taken. These regulations are not unreasonable, and they are always in conformity with the sacramental nature of the marriage ceremony. In many churches it is forbidden to take pictures while the Host is exposed or communion is being given because the attitude of every one involved at such a time should be one of adoration and not of taking pictures.

There are two things to remember about the wedding day. The first is that the wedding day is the bride's day. This phrase seems to imply that the groom is being left out; its tone is perhaps too casual since this is the day when two people in love start the long path back to God together. However, the expression "the bride's day" in general has a very benevolent and restricted meaning. It is in no sense a slight to the groom— usually there is sufficient sentimentalism available at a wedding for everybody. Most of the symbolism, sentimentalism, and pomp and ceremony of the wedding day is, of course, traditionally centered about the bride—what she does, what she wears, and how she thinks. And since girls have been conditioned from the time they were five to be enthusiastic about the symbolism of marriage, it is only natural that on her wedding day any girl be allowed to voice her variations of the theme and, in turn, be given support by everyone concerned.

The second item of major importance on this great day is the ceremony itself. There are really two choices available. One is a simple wedding ceremony before a priest in which the contract is bound sacramentally. It is done simply in a sacred and holy manner and efficiently.

The other choice (and there really isn't any choice) is the Nuptial Mass. All Catholics are brought up to believe that a Mass has an infinite value. They are also taught that any function, or any day, or any decision of importance in their lives, should be shared with God in the Mass. Thus it is common practice to go to Mass after the engagement day, on the morning of an important examination, on the day of an interview of critical importance to the person's future, or in thanksgiving for some success achieved. It is incredible then that a Catholic would set out on a journey as important as marriage and as binding as life itself and destined to last until death—without sharing this moment of agreement, this day of hopes, plans, and love with his or her Creator. If the Mass has infinite value, and it has, then it is an appropriate gift to offer to the Lord accompanied by the prayers of the couple themselves and the Church as they enter into an agreement which is calculated to carry them to eternity.

"Male and Female Created He Them"

Everyone agrees that man and woman are different. That difference (which is composed of many differences) is interesting and captivating, assuring and salutary—but it does not divide the sexes into hostile camps. Yet many modern writers, particularly those writing on marriage, imply or even insist that man and woman are opposite when actually they are merely different. Both can be tender, sentimental, angry, knowledgeable, reactionary, proud, defiant, and loving. They don't approach any of these moods or reactions in opposite ways but they do display them in different ways. There is a feminine attitude and the male position; woman's intuition and man's calculation; male enthusiasm and female excitement; male motion and female emotion.

It is precisely *this difference* in the way men and women act or react which makes them suited for one another, which stimulates their attractiveness for one another, which makes their common life together interesting and which is the whetstone for their compatibility. Thus the man, having carefully chartered a course of action for his children, for example, indicates where to go and how and the woman, while in complete agreement with him, may indicate with special judgment how far or when. A woman can temper the steel of a man's decision and convert a ruthless act into a positive and productive one. On the other hand, a man can convert an emotional, semi-hysterical tirade into an effective weapon of indignation by bringing into play the reserves of unemotional facts and well-correlated figures. The well-known feminine propensity for clemency can be converted into tempered demonstrations for mercy, which also serve the needs of justice, when the proper support of authority and the rights of the community are also borne in mind.

Too much is made of the opposition of the sexes; too much, indeed, is made of the competition between the sexes. In His Providential wisdom God has shown that in happy marriages, man and woman truly *complement* one another, and that one is not and never can be as effective when working alone.

There are things about each other to be learned. A man has pride in three things—his wife, his family, and his livelihood. His effectiveness in earning his livelihood is determined by the nature of his work, the equipment that he brings to that work, his special talent if any, the occupational hazards, and the remuneration and opportunity that livelihood affords him to make the proper plans for his family and his future. It is not, furthermore, as though a man sheds one set of responsibilities as he leaves for work and assumes another, only to exchange them again at the end of the day. The responsibilities involved in earning his livelihood may be several, but they are peculiar to the nature of that performance. He always carries with him the added responsibilities which *are* his performance—his family. His concerns for the one are inevitably and constantly mingled with concerns for the other.

A conscientious man, on returning home after a hard day of work, may find it difficult to unburden himself of his twin responsibilities unless his wife, by an intuitive and loving use of womanly wiles, convinces him that in his battle he is not alone and that together they can do anything. A man looks for daily pride in his home, his family, and his livelihood. When he fails to find it, frustration, irritability, anxiety, and insecurity begin to gnaw at his personality.

A woman also finds pride in her home, her family and her husband, but it is her nature to discharge her responsibilities through the best weapon at her command—her love. It is the nature of love that the more it is expended, the more it is returned. A man and woman's life together does not consist of the man doing things and the woman receiving the fruits of his efforts; rather the man's task in life is one thing and the woman's something else again. When both are done competently and harmoniously a happy home results.

A woman, too, has her occupational irritability—children

on a rainy day, the incompatibility of children in the neighborhood, or the plans for a meal going awry. In addition, symptoms of the menstrual period may irritate her. As indicated in Chapter Eleven, these symptoms may be mild or troublesome. In any case, there must be understanding by the husband. For severe symptoms, the physician must prescribe medication. And though the menstrual period is peculiarly feminine, it does not make a woman the *opposite* of a man; it simply makes the source of her irritability *different* from, for example, the source of a man's headaches and "grumpiness."

One also hears of the "active" male and "passive" female. It is referred to in all phases of behavior but most predominantly in regard to a couple's sexual life. The "doing" of the male and the "receptiveness" of the female is often referred to as is the female's "rejection of the passive role," her lack of "receptivity," and the unemotional, unresponsive, or even (heaven help us) frigid female. As we have mentioned elsewhere, such women, particularly frigid women, are likely to be psychopaths. Doctors who see women exclusively in their female roles do not commonly encounter them.

No one denies that the man is active in the act of marital love, but to say that the woman is passive is unrealistic and does her a great injustice. The woman is active; she is not passive. She is more slowly aroused and the rhythm of her motion may be slower, more gentle, and perhaps occasionally less perceptible, but it is folly to say that the woman does not actively take part in the act of marital love. It cannot be too often repeated that there are two to be loved and two *who are loving*. The husband acting as the lover must in a sense play his beloved like a well-loved violin and match his rhythm to hers, whether it be slow and deliberate or accelerated and vigorous.

The people who talk so glibly about the unresponsive woman actually are referring to the *unaroused* woman. Those of us privileged to see so many happy women in happy marriages find that the couple communicating their love and their needs to one another are able to fulfill themselves in the act of love in marriage. Under such circumstances the unresponsive and unresponding woman simply does not exist.

The proper arousal and the proper stimulation of the married woman in the act of love to the point where she may achieve her right and heritage as a woman in love calls for consideration, kindness, and interest by the husband. The woman herself must have a proper understanding of modesty and chastity and the true meaning of trust. She must eliminate false modesty and elevate mutual trust and love to their proper place. There must be understanding, patience, gentleness, and communication on both sides. I have never seen a happily married woman, one who had satisfactory and happy love relations with her husband, who felt that she was in any way dominated by her husband. Such women were convinced, impressed even, that in a proper expression of love they were able to do so much *for one another*. This I submit is more logically and more likely the plan of Providence.

Man and woman are created different; they are made one by the bond of marriage and the common life. Together they learn to laugh and cry; solace and support are mutual gifts, and all the joys of a special camaraderie are theirs. A peculiar happiness is theirs in doing things for one another. Together they love, and together they live.

Once usually to each couple is this opportunity granted; only once do they face the challenge of *their* future.

The wedding day comes and goes; the soul-searching ends, for the time—the compatible soul has been found. The honeymoon is upon them. The common life begins.

The Honeymoon

The honeymoon is a valuable and wonderful institution. It is here to stay. We are in favor of it.

A honeymoon should be personal, memorable, wonderful— and inexpensive.

If it were possible to capture a time-and-place experience and lock it away in your home as a memorable keepsake of your life together, I am sure that the honeymoon would take its place among the marriage treasures along with the day of engagement and the wedding day. On the wedding trip a couple should attempt to do something that is simple and at the same time different and memorable. It may be associated with going to a particular place or going just any place and doing something which is meaningful to their love. There should be no thought of meeting with other people. There is no necessity for entertaining or being entertained by others. At such a time, who needs others?

The honeymoon should not, unless there are compelling reasons, sentimental and otherwise, involve considerable traveling or frequent side trips. Such traveling is tiring and customarily lends little or nothing to the true purpose of a honeymoon. The couple should save their strength, interest, and energies for one another.

There is no reason for the honeymoon to be expensive. The honeymoon should be a status symbol of nothing but love. The place for it should not be selected on the basis of what people are doing this year. The couple truly in love should not care where others go or do. Their interest should be wholly in where they are going for *their* honeymoon, where they can prepare for their life together. It might very well be a motel twenty miles away. There is even some merit in the groom's choosing the honeymoon spot and surprising the bride with it. If he chooses with acumen and a little imagination, all she needs to know is the nature of the climate. Money should be spent on a wedding trip to make it different and memorable if money will do this. Otherwise, the cost of the wedding trip is little more than the first item in the family budget.

The newly-weds returning from their honeymoon turn the key in the lock of their new home and generally find themselves not knowing quite what to expect. This is one of the interesting things in life—not knowing what to expect—and it can be one of the nicest experiences in marriage. Newlyweds should not expect to pick up where their parents left off. They will find their home different from their parents', because different people are creating it. The attitudes in some instances will be the same but more often there will be an important nuance of difference. A newly married couple have a creative drive to build a home that is peculiarly theirs, and they are sometimes confused because they really don't know where to start. One of the greatest difficulties is that up to now each person has been accustomed to expressing himself or herself, and now their home must be an expression of their unity. Setting up a home while trying different routines of family living may take as long as six months. This is the time to try to perpetuate the spirit of the honeymoon.

The spirit of the honeymoon is its most important aspect. Let the honeymoon be the means by which you get close to one another. Let that closeness be a concerted and mutual effort to produce a result so binding that it will set a pattern for the rest of your lives. Get away from the madding crowd, get close to one another. Take the Godspeeds, blessings, and tears of your family and leave the neighbors and wedding guests with their good wishes, practical jokes, and advice. Yours is the serious business of becoming one. Yours is the delightful privilege of beginning the common life. The honeymoon is for each other. Plan your world and test your dreams; explore each other's minds and bodies and souls. Set a pattern of behavior that will help you to make the jump from dreams to reality—which will be your task within a very few days. Let the honeymoon be for you and the beloved a good beginning, a memorable event, and the first step in the solution of the responsibilities to come.

8

The Facts of Love and Life

A doctor is privileged to look upon marriage from many aspects. Among marriage counselors and people who see the problems of marriage, his position is almost unique; he sees a parade of happy people quietly in love producing the fruit of their love and nurturing families. Of course, a doctor sees the problems of marriage as well. And as may be expected, many of these concern its physical aspects.

These problems usually arise from a lack of knowledge of the structure of the body, ignorance pertaining to matters of the marital act, or actual physical errors in performing the act. All or any of these situations produce dissatisfaction or frustration. They can be the underlying basis for unhappiness and much of the petty bickering and in-fighting that precipitate marital squalls and emotional outbursts. It should be emphasized that marital problems seldom arise because of any major physical abnormality or faulty development. A poor attitude towards love and marriage combined with ignorance remain the major sources of friction.

A physician's task in attempting to help people in such situations is made easier or more difficult by numerous factors. This is simply because there are numerous factors which affect people's behavior and motivation. These factors may be physical, social, economic, psychological, religious, ethical, or mental. So a doctor has to deal with the physical and must be constantly aware of the extra-physical. But as a result of his training and vocation, a physician is probably more aware than any other person of the influence of these factors on a person's physical and mental health.

Our approach to marriage in this chapter, therefore, is primarily physical as would be expected. We are going to discuss the facts of life, so called, but occasional exploration into other areas may be necessary; so, if in what follows, we digress into areas ordinarily recognized as other than the physician's field, it is not because we are trying to invade some other expert's field but simply because we are trying to remind ourselves, and you, that we are here talking about a very human function, a uniquely human institution, involving people who are not disembodied spirits but who have problems any one of which may touch many aspects of living.

People who marry classify themselves into three groups. The first group comprises those who marry with a fairly clear concept of just what they are getting into from a medical, social, and economic point of view. This group is unfortunately much too small. In the second group are those who enter into marriage with little or no concept of its real values. This group is still larger than we like to see, although the establishment of premarital courses, premarital lectures, personal conferences, examinations, and Pre-Cana Conferences have done much toward correcting a situation that was unhappy and in some areas growing to be intolerable. The third group comprises those people who wed with a smattering of knowledge of one or more aspects of marriage. They may have good intentions, some deep-seated misconceptions, and considerable incomplete information or misinformation.

This book is being written and published under Catholic auspices, and, as a physician, I think there are several things that deserve comment in this regard. First of all, the ideas contained in this essay, while Catholic in their approach, represent concepts that are not mortgaged to Catholics; neither do we own the exclusive rights to them. The Church, in its position as the champion of the Natural Moral Law, shows its influence in these pages to the degree that any ethical or moral concept derived from the Natural Moral Law is apt to be repetitiously emphasized in this series. Secondly, the term "Catholic" as an adjective in front of a physician's name does not put him under any particular cloud so far as the freedom of his practice or medical thinking is concerned. The Church requires that the physician, in his life and practice, fulfill the Natural Moral Law no more than the laborer, the businessman, or the technician. The author knows of no physician who has ever been told by the Church how he must practice medicine, or what he is to say under such circumstances as these. Thirdly, the simplest answer to all doubts and charges that have been made against "Catholic medicine" are best resolved on the proposition that God, by definition, being All-wise, could not, therefore, have established one set of Laws in medicine or science and, at the same time established another set of Laws in ethics and religion which would be mutually conflicting or contradictory. God, by definition, cannot be contradictory and, therefore, it shall be eternally true that good medicine and good morality, both coming from the same Author, must always go hand in hand.

Although it may appear to the contrary to those outside the

Church, the Catholic religion is not a negative religion. It is not constantly telling us what not to do. On the contrary, it is a religion with a very positive doctrine. Very appropriately, for our purposes in this chapter, that positive doctrine of the Catholic Church is *love*. God came upon earth for the love of man, and He died for the love of man. He said that the greatest virtue was Charity, which is another word for love; the greatest commandment is love of God and love of neighbor; and He established the contract of marriage as an institution of love for two humans.

Love between two people prior to marriage is shown in a number of ways. Kissing and caressing, certainly; novelists would be lost without them—and so would people. But a little reflection I think will convince everyone that love between two people prior to marriage is fundamentally shown by acts of kindness and thoughtfulness and characterized by the idea that they would give anything or do anything for each other. When two people marry, they achieve new rights and new obligations. Neither the rights nor the obligations are one-sided. The rights involved are given by one to the other. The obligations incurred are binding on both partners and justice demands that the contractual rights of both partners be respected, and the obligations of both be fulfilled.

As two people in marriage swear to one another in a contract to love each other until death, they learn to love God better. As they learn to love God better, God sends them a two-fold reward with which to cement their love for one another and to increase their love for Him. The first of these rewards is commonly referred to by a term which has a rather dead, common sound—pregnancy. Whether viewed from the vantage point of the Natural Moral Law—or the Catholic position, if you will—or from the attitude of love, pregnancy is nothing more or less than the loan of a soul which God gives to two people in love as a reward for their love for each other and their love for Him. They are loaned a soul to bring into the world, to nurture and educate, and return to Him.

The second reward that God gives to those who, loving each other, learn to love Him is again generally referred to by a rather coarse, harsh-sounding term—sexual intercourse. Through the centuries many inept terms have been coined to express this concept—coitus, marital congress, marital relations, being with the husband, being with the wife, or even the term borrowed from the lower kingdom of animals, copulation; none of these terms call the act what it really is— an act of love between two people, one of the most sublime within the power of man, the gift of a kind God to His creatures. The act has always defied description and has never adequately been described or defined. As many times as it has occurred, to as many couples in love since the beginning of time, it has not lost its celestial flavor and benediction. It is almost miraculously a constant source of sublime pleasure with which a couple may bind their love.

To talk about marriage is to talk about love. Those who enter into marriage to get something out of it or with an angle to play are doomed to failure in marriage. Marriage is not something you "get anything out of." The greatest happiness in marriage is to be found as a result of what you are able to put into it for the person you love. In the marriage of "true minds" there is no room for talk about the predatory male, the uxorious husband, the termagant shrew, or the unresponsive female. This is not a question of negative values; it is a question of two genuine people whose love is based upon a stout trust and knowledge and desire to give themselves to each other. Marriage is a matter of two people who have a real pride in each other's love and a down-to-earth appreciation of the privilege that is theirs in being a man or woman. With customary acuity Byron said ". . . all who joy would win must share it. Happiness was born a twin." The unhappy Byron may not be the best person to quote under these conditions. However, Byron was a genius, and we are always privileged to borrow from genius.

There are two people in love, therefore, two people to be loved and two people to do the loving. If they are to function as God intended them to in the act of love in marriage, it is necessary to turn to a review of the anatomy of the organs involved in the act of love in marriage.

The Male Anatomy

The primary organs of reproduction in the male are known as the testicles. These are grayish-white structures about the size of a large walnut, slightly flattened and two in number. They are found in a sac of skin called the scrotum which hangs between the legs of every male. Normally, one testicle is somewhat larger than the other, as is true of all double organs of the body, and usually the left testicle is slightly lower than the right. The testicles are, obviously, on the outside of the body. There is a reason for this. The testicles of the unborn boy child are developed in an area much higher than where they are found in adult life, in an area much closer to his ribs. At or just beyond birth, the testicles move down into the groin (where men commonly have hernias) and subsequently down into the scrotum. The testicles, in the scrotum, are thus outside of the body. The testicles are in the scrotum because the temperature there is about two degrees lower than in the body proper. It has been pointed out that if the testicles developed within the body, the higher temperature there would atrophy them, that is, they would lose the nourishment required for their proper development. A boy to whom this happened would reach adult life permanently incapable of ever becoming a father. That is why we hear occasionally of a young boy who undergoes surgery to have his testicles brought down to the scrotum.

The testicle has basically two functions. The first function is as a gland. Now everyone knows what a gland is: a lump in your neck which becomes quite sore when a sore throat is present. This is correct, but more technically, a gland is a collection of cells brought together in a certain area of the body for a specific purpose. Thus the gland in the neck as a collection of cells is brought together for the defense of the body against throat infections.

The glandular portion of the testicle is a collection of cells brought together for two purposes. The first is the production of the male seed or sperm, and the second is the production of the male hormones. Hormones are substances secreted by several glands in the body; they have a specific, highly specialized purpose. The male hormones are responsible for the development of the secondary male characteristics, that is, they contribute the maleness to men just as the female hormones contribute the femaleness to women. The production of male sperm or seed is obviously a major function of the testicle and one of its specific purposes. As we will see later, the testicle produces the sperm in prodigious numbers.

The second portion of the testicle, representing about one-half of its total anatomical structure, is made up of a system of channels or tubules which are extremely tiny and whose function is to carry the sperm or male seed to the outside world. These tiny channels or tubules (of which it has been said that there are twenty-two miles in each testicle) coalesce and group together to form eventually one large channel known as the vas deferens. Thus the sperm, which is the smallest cell in the human body, approximately 1/500 of an inch long, produced in the hundreds of millions, swim through these channels and eventually reach the vas deferens.

The *vas*, as it is commonly called, is a large channel that runs from the scrotum through the groin and over and behind the pubic bone. The pubic bone is the bone that connects the hips in front; in both sexes, the skin covering it is covered with hair. As the vas deferens goes behind the pubic bone it empties into the passage (urethra) to the urinary bladder at the base of the bladder. The urinary bladder, which is located directly behind the pubic bone empties to the outside world through a passage, and it is into this passage that the sperm in a male eventually pass as they come up from the scrotum. The passage into which the sperm eventually empty is known as the urethra. As the vas goes from the scrotum to the urethra, it is met by a number of glands the names of which are not particularly important. The function of these glands, however, is to produce a glary, grayish liquid which is called seminal fluid and is the solution in which the sperm may swim and in which they are carried to the outside world through the urethra.

From what has been said above, the urethra in the male obviously has two functions. It carries the urine from the urinary bladder to the outside world and it is the channel by which the male seed or sperm in the spermatic or seminal fluid is passed to the outside. It is important, however, to realize that the male may not perform both functions at the same time. A system of valves, muscular controls, and nervous mechanisms over which the male has neither knowledge nor control enables him to pass either his sperm or his urine through the urethra but not both at once.

The proper organ for intercourse in the male is known as the *penis*. The penis is a soft, finger-like structure which hangs down from the pubic bone (the bone that connects the hips in front) in front of the scrotum. The penis is normally three to four inches in length and is soft in the non-erectile state. It is made up of three parts. The first part we have already mentioned in some detail, namely, the urethra or passage which carries either the urine or the male seed to the outside. The other two parts of the penis are composed of two structures containing large blood vessels which, under conditions of sexual excitement, fill up with blood, as a result of which the penis becomes large, hard, firm, and erect. At this point the male is said to be in a state of erection or the state of sexual excitement and is said to be ready for the act of love. Erection of the male penis enables the male to penetrate his wife's hymen (the partial covering of the front passage in the female) in the act of love in marriage, enter her vagina (or front passage), and deposit at the top of her front passage, at the neck of her womb, his seed or sperm. The very tip of the penis is sexually the most sensitive part of the male body. Occasionally in marriage, this area must be stimulated by the wife in order to arouse her husband to sexual excitement.

We have mentioned the term seminal fluid which the male produces each time he makes love with his wife. Just prior to the actual performance of the marital act and under conditions of sexual excitement, the male may produce a slight amount of rather thin, glary material which is not seminal fluid but a secretion of some of the accessory glands of the reproductive system; it acts for lubricating purposes or constitutes a part of the fluid in which the sperm eventually swim. Seminal fluid which contains the sperm and which is deposited in the wife's vagina in the act of love is much thicker.

In the early days of marriage the male may not easily penetrate his wife's hymen for a number of reasons which we will presently discuss. The extra time and effort required may cause him to lose his seed before he enters his wife's body. In other words he may not be able to "hold off" until his wife is also ready, properly aroused, and prepared for the act of love. And so, because of excitement, he deposits his seed on the outside of her body or even on the bedding. To do this deliberately, of course, is contrary to the natural moral law and is known as the sin of Onan. However, under the conditions as described, this is an accident, and, of course, accidents don't count. As the result of such an accident, many a honeymoon couple has been quite distraught to find on the bedding the following morning a thick, glary material which is quite disturbing to them. Sometimes they conclude that this is pus and that one or both members of the partnership are infected, and lo, the ship of marriage has hardly left port and they are already in a hurricane. So, forlorn and distraught, away from the security of friends and family, they seek out the nearest physician and relate their tale of woe. Their problem is solved when told that this is the normal state of seminal fluid. Under normal conditions within a few days this matter is straightened out; both partners become acclimated to their loving, and the male is able to penetrate his wife's body and to deposit his seed at the neck of her womb in her vagina.

The average male, every time he makes love with his wife, will produce approximately one teaspoon of a thick, glary material which is grayish-white in color and has an odor best described as "fishy." This is normal seminal fluid. In each of these ejaculations, as they are called, the average male may produce up to 400,000,000 sperm, only one of which needs to penetrate an egg in order to produce a pregnancy. This is a tremendous effort on the part of nature, particularly in view of the fact that only one sperm can penetrate an egg, and the average woman, as we will see later, produces approximately ten eggs a year—the first proof that man is one of the most infertile animals in the animal kingdom and the one least likely to reproduce himself. (The egg is fertilizable for one day—the life of the sperm may extend the fertility to two or more days.)

A female is apt to have only one fertile day each month, and most couples have intercourse much more often than once a month (the average being twice or three times a week), so the question is often asked, what happens to the sperm which has been deposited in the vagina at a time when pregnancy cannot take place? The answer is very simple. Some of the seminal fluid flows out of the girl as a part of the discharge found after intercourse, and the vagina apparently absorbs the rest. In any case, it is worth pointing out here, as will be pointed out again, the fact that the vagina is one of the best self-cleansing organs in the body and is capable of cleaning whatever is excess in it at any time, except when infected.

Another frequent question is, what happens if the male, who is capable of producing such prodigious quantities of sperm, has any particular period of continence in which he does not ejaculate these large quantities of sperm? Again, the body has the ability to absorb large quantities of sperm. It continuously absorbs large quantities of cells which we break down and replace with new ones. So this function is not associated merely with the reproductive tract but is, naturally, a part of the body's business.

The Female Anatomy

The female reproductive organs are more numerous and more fascinating than the male's; furthermore, we know more about them. The greater number and variety of the female reproductive organs is to be expected because the female is not only equipped to derive as much pleasure as the male in the love act, but she is equipped also for the added task of nurturing a baby for nine months, delivering that baby at term through the process of labor, and nourishing the baby after birth.

The female reproductive organs are generally divided into external and internal categories. The first external organ to be discussed is the breast. It has two functions, the first of which is primarily sexual. The breast is one of the most powerful areas of sexual stimulation in the female. In order to arouse the female to that point of emotional and physical excitement where she is prepared to enter into the marital act and to get from it her right, due, and heritage as a woman in love, the breast must be stimulated by the husband in the love play prior to the act of love. When the breasts are properly stimulated, the nipples contract somewhat and become erect. The breast may be kissed or caressed or fondled by the husband in the love play prior to the act of love; and while the amount of sexual response varies from one woman to another, in general, the breast is a powerful erogenous area.

The second function of the breast is to feed the young after birth. It is unfortunate that bridge clubs and other groups, in the last twenty to thirty years, have made breast feeding unpopular in the United States. Until recent years, any woman who dared to breast feed her baby was considered anathema by her clubmates and friends. It is somewhat heartening to notice a slight trend back toward breast feeding, for despite all the vaunted prowess of modern science, a formula has not yet been devised which is complete in every sense to take the place of the food which a kind God has given a mother for her own baby. It is generally conceded that the mother and baby feel much closer to one another when the baby is breast fed, that the babies are generally happier, and that the mother is apt to have a much more thorough knowledge of her baby and its habits. The three most common arguments given by women against breast feeding are that it is inconvenient, ties the mother down, and disturbs or alters her figure. These have been shown to be specious, unsupported statements usually most vigorously defended by women who have never nursed a baby. (It is more or less a constant observation by most doctors that most women who have never nursed a baby are opposed to seeing anyone else nurse a baby.)

The other reproductive organs in the female are found in the pelvic area, which is the area demarcated by the hip bones on either side, by the backbone in the rear, and the pubic bone (which connects the hips in front). Specifically, the external organs of reproduction that are found in this area are found in the space between the legs of the female. In the female there are three openings in this area and these are: the opening from the urinary bladder, which is close to the pubic bone; below this, the opening to the front passage or vagina, partially covered by a membrane known as the hymen; and below that, the opening to the rectum. On either side of these three openings are found two folds of skin generally referred to as the "lips" of the front passage and technically known as the vulva. These lips, or vulvae, come together in the midline at a point at the top of the pubic bone where the hair is most dense. Where these lips join is found a tiny structure known as the clitoris. The clitoris is almost hidden in the soft tissue and only the very tip of it is palpable between the closing lips of the front passage. It is rarely more than 1/4 of an inch in length in most women and about 1/16 of an inch to 1/8 of an inch wide. It is quite sensitive from the sexual point of view, and in that sense is a very important structure for any woman. It has one function and one function only, and that is as a source of sexual excitement for the woman in the love play prior to the marital act and for the successful achievement of orgasm (or sexual satisfaction) during the act of love in marriage.

The clitoris is one of the most, if not the most, powerful areas for sexual excitement in the female. Under conditions of sexual excitement, or in other words, during the love play prior to the act of love in marriage, it expands to twice its normal size, becoming firm and erect just as does the penis in the male. But it must be stimulated by the husband's hand prior to the act of love in marriage and by his penis during the marital act, if the woman is to get the normal pleasure which is her right, due, and heritage as a married woman. Her husband not only has a duty to stimulate his wife prior to and during the act of love in marriage but, furthermore, she has an equal duty to allow him to do it and to encourage him and to teach him to do it and do it properly.

Directly below the clitoris is the opening from the urinary passage in the female which, in this instance, is simply an opening. It is, however, sexually sensitive and is surrounded by blood vessel tissue which also becomes erect under sexual excitement; consequently, this area must also be stimulated by the husband's hand and penis prior to and during the act of love in marriage.

Directly below the opening from the urinary bladder (known as the urethra), is the opening to the front passage or vagina in the female. This opening is roughly circular. It is partially covered by a membrane which in texture is not unlike the lining of the mouth but much thinner. This membrane, soft and velvety, containing a few muscular fibers, is known as the hymen (Hymen—the Greek god of marriage). The hymen, therefore, is the marriage structure. It was intended by nature to be stretched or torn or broken with the first attempts at the act of love and is, therefore, the structure which is opened by the male penis as it is introduced into the vagina in the first attempts at loving in marriage.

In most women the opening to the hymen is a roughly circular opening with sort of scalloped edges. Obviously, this type of hymenal opening, especially if it is soft and thin, is one which is readily stretched. When it is stretched, there is slight discomfort but rarely any severe pain. There may also be some slight staining, but again, rarely is there any bleeding of any degree. Occasionally, a hymenal opening is a series of slits or linear openings which join together in the center and are shaped something like the letter "Y." Obviously an opening of this shape, when stretched, will tend to tear along the three linear openings and cause somewhat more discomfort and a slight amount of bleeding.

Some rare hymens have not one but multiple openings, two or more with bridges of tissue between them. Obviously, this type of hymen must be broken and the bridges of tissue between the openings torn so that one rather large opening results. Here again, the discomfort or momentary pain may be somewhat more than with the more common types and the bleeding may be sufficient to look like the beginning of a period.

Occasionally, a wife's hymen, regardless of the shape of the opening, is thick or rigid, or the muscles which support the hymen are heavy and rigid, and the couple finds that the satisfactory performance of the act of love is impossible. In such cases, the woman should not feel that she is a freak of nature, incompletely made, more male than female, or one of those rare people so irresponsibly reported in the newspapers who have elements of both the male and female sex. A thick hymen is simply a manifestation of individual variance; it is much less common than a familiar variance in the size of a nose and much simpler to correct. Under these conditions, the hymen must be cut. Actually, in the operation something more than the hymen is cut; generally, the muscles at the base of the hymen are split and enough room is created at the hymenal orifice for normal marital intercourse to take place readily. This should cause no great concern to either partner because the procedure is quite simple, it does not take a great deal of time, and generally requires no more than two or three days of hospitalization and often less than that. This operation, though not common, is not rare either, and is so simply effective that most people who have needed such correction and obtained it have thought it a small price to pay for much happiness.

In less severe degrees of the same problem (rigid hymen) the use of graduated vaginal dilators (tubes of increasing size fitted into the vagina to stretch the hymen and vagina) may occasionally be used quite successfully.

As has been mentioned, there may be some discomfort or momentary pain, or slight staining or bleeding, with the first attempts at intercourse due to splitting or tearing of the hymen. This is a fact, and it is a definite one, but it should not upset either spouse, nor should it cause the woman any undue panic or sense of foreboding. A forewarning that this may occur is usually the only requirement that is necessary in its management. It is the woman who is unaware that there may be some discomfort or bleeding who is apt to be in danger of panic. If she is ignorant of this fact, she probably won't realize that her preparation and her period of love play is also necessary, and more than likely, she will have no knowledge of position in the act of love. In most instances where the girl is unprepared, it is unfortunately also true that the bridegroom is apt to be unprepared as well. As a matter of fact, even if one is knowledgeable, the fact that the other is not and, therefore, has no understanding of what the prepared member is talking about or trying to do, leads to a virtual impasse.

As we have already indicated, if the girl is unprepared she is apt to become tearful or hysterical or badly frightened. The effect on the bridegroom is apt to be tragic, for he has just married and is now in the position to love the person he holds dearest in the world in the most perfect way that God has given him. If he is made to feel he is causing pain, anguish, and fright in his actions, it is not surprising if he develops an emotional state which is not too dissimilar from his wife's. So a couple, because they are uninformed, go through a rather harrowing experience on the initial voyage of the ship of their marriage.

Whether or not the actual attempt at loving induces pain or discomfort or a mere burning sensation, it is not uncommon after the first attempts at intercourse for a woman to notice some soreness in the hymenal area the following morning. Having become aware of this soreness, it is only natural for her to mention it to her husband who immediately, and perhaps in some haste and not a little fright, may suggest that they forego intercourse until the soreness disappears. This natural reaction is sometimes referred to as the first error in marriage. Unless the situation is unusual, and only experience will elicit this for the couple, the best general advice is that since the soreness is generally not severe, the couple should continue to have lovings within reason, and as the hymen is stretched and heals, usually within three to five days, the soreness will disappear.

It is not our intention to leave an impression that the initial loving in marriage is so attended by pain and bleeding that the well-equipped bride and groom carry a morphine syrette and a spare pint of blood for the exigencies of the honeymoon. What we do mean to imply is that ignorance can transform the normal sequence of natural events into a mutual hysterical trance. We mean that as kindness and consideration typify love so the art of loving is the art of being gentle. The couple should in no way feel that the initial attempts at the marital act are a fearsome experience. Nature does not leave the couple alone. At the base of the hymen are two glands (Bartholin's glands) whose function is very important to any married couple. The function of Bartholin's glands is to produce a liberal quantity of mucus which acts as a natural lubricant for the act of love in marriage. These glands are buried in a deep tissue but open into the hymen and, under conditions of sexual excitement, they produce a tremendous amount of secretion. This secretion acts as a natural lubricant which nature has set up in order to make more easy the passage of the male penis through the hymen and into the vagina.

The secretion may be psychologically induced, especially just before the marriage, for example, as the girl talks on the telephone to her fiancé or as she bids him goodnight at the end of a date. It thus represents the first sign of sexual excitement in the female. During the period of love play when the clitoris and the urethra and the tissues around the urethra are stimulated by the husband's hand prior to the marital act, it constitutes the bulk of the sexual secretion.

In the course of the sexual love play in marriage, as the girl begins to get excited, the tissues around her hymen (which support her hymen and which are naturally erectile tissues) fill up with blood, and as a result the entire hymenal area becomes swollen and the "outer-most" of all the tissues. In other words, the lips of the vagina open up like a flower, and the hymen, bathed with the lubricating secretion mentioned above, becomes soft and pliable. In ancient times, poets wrote about the deflowering of the maidenhead. The maidenhead, of course, is the hymen; the term deflowering was used because under conditions of sexual excitement, near the peak of the excitement the vulva, the lips of the front passage, fill up with blood and open the inner lips in such a way that the hymen is exposed for the penetration of the penis. Thus then, an anatomical mechanism has been built into the woman by the very providential Creator. It is a very delicate mechanism which, when properly stimulated by her husband acting as her lover, secures for her the happiness and pleasure which a kind God has ordained for both members of the partnership in the physical act of love in marriage.

The Internal Female Reproductive Organs

The hymen is the gateway to the reproductive tract and the opening to the first of the internal organs, which is called the vagina. The vagina is a potential cavity, that is, a hollow structure whose walls are normally collapsed one on the other but are capable of being stretched to become the birth canal. The vagina is normally three to five inches in length and extends from the hymen to the neck of the womb, which is at the uppermost portion of the vagina and which occupies about one-half inch of the upper portion of the vagina. The walls of the vagina are very specially constructed. They are made up of a number of tight folds not unlike the pleats in an accordion-pleated skirt. Thus, when a baby is born through the vagina, the vaginal wall so stretches that the baby's head, the largest part of the newborn infant, may pass through it without tearing the wall. The vagina has three functions. The first is the menstrual function; the vagina is the passage through which the menstrual flow comes from the womb to the outside every month. Secondly, it is the organ of intercourse into which the penis is inserted in the act of love in marriage. The vagina, therefore, in this regard, is also an area of powerful sexual stimulation. Thirdly, as already described, it forms the birth canal.

At the top of the vagina is the womb. Specifically, the neck of the womb is the portion which is in the vagina; the rest of the womb is up in the major part of the abdomen or the belly. The womb is located almost in the exact geographic center of the pelvis; thus, if we take the pubic bone as the anterior or forwardmost portion of the pelvis, we have directly behind this bone the urinary bladder, directly behind the urinary bladder the womb, behind the womb the rectum or back passage, and then the backbone. So the womb and the vagina below it are bordered internally in front by the urinary bladder and in back by the rectum.

The womb is a muscle. It is one of the most powerful muscles known to human medicine. Normally, it is a structure about three inches long, two inches wide, and one inch thick which is narrowed at one end so that it looks not unlike a pear. It looks, as a matter of fact, not unlike a pear which is somewhat flattened. The narrow end of the pear is known as the neck of the womb or the cervix and is the portion of the womb that extends down into the top of the vagina as previously mentioned. The neck of the womb is a very important structure, for this is the portion of the womb with which the male penis comes into contact during the act of love in marriage, and where the penis deposits the male sperm. In the neck of the womb, furthermore, is a tiny opening through which the sperm swim up into the womb to meet the egg and through which the menstrual flow comes every month. The opening in the neck of the womb, pin-point in size, must be, in the course of labor, opened up big enough to allow the head of a newborn baby to go through it; thus, the neck of the womb is the anatomical representation of labor. Most women are familiar with the neck of the womb as a structure which is always examined after childbirth (usually six weeks after the birth of the baby), and is not infrequently burnt or cauterized in order to clear up infection.

The body of the womb is found within the abdominal cavity itself, right behind the urinary bladder. The womb has a cavity in it, and this cavity has three openings. The first opening, which we have already mentioned, is the neck of the womb, the portion in the vagina; the other two openings are at the top of the womb and lead to the tubes which extend out laterally on either side of the pelvis to the ovaries. The cavity of the womb has a capacity of approximately one teaspoonful. It is normally lined with a thick, juicy, soft lining which sloughs out when not used at menstrual time.

The tubes, or more properly the Fallopian tubes, are thin-walled, muscular structures about five to eight inches in length which have finger-like projections at the terminal end. They have a very fine lining of cells which, with a secretion and hairs, assist in the migration upward of the sperm which has been deposited in the neck of the womb. The actions of these cells, and the contractions of the tubes, also aid in the migration of the egg from the ovary downward to the womb. The finger-like projections at the end of the tubes sweep over the lateral margins of the pelvis and occasionally sweep over closely to the surface of the ovary in an attempt to pick up those eggs which are deposited by the ovary in the pelvic area or which are found on the surface of the ovary itself.

The ovaries are lozenge-shaped structures about 1 inch to 1½ inches long, grayish-white, firm, and two in number, one on either side of the pelvis. The function of the ovaries is twofold. First, they produce the eggs and are, therefore, similar to the testicles which produce the sperm in the male. Secondly, they produce hormones which influence menstruation and which also can aid in the early development of the embryo should the egg become fertilized and start to develop in the womb. These are the hormones which maintain the femaleness of women just as the hormones produced by the testicle are responsible for the maleness of men.

The ovaries are unusual structures. They ordinarily function about ten times a year. It is said that the average girl (who lives only in textbooks, really) will have thirteen menstrual periods in the course of the year. But for many girls, there are two or three months a year in which they may not produce eggs. Furthermore, evidence indicates that the ovaries work alternately—one ovary produces an egg one month and the other ovary the next month. And it is known that not infrequently in every woman one ovary works for three or four months at a time before the other finally takes over.

The egg is produced by the ovary about halfway between the periods. This, of course, varies tremendously within the normal interim between a girl's periods. As we will see, there is probably a relationship between the time the girl ovulates and the time of her next expected period but no constant relationship between ovulation and the previous menstrual period.

Although the estimates as to how long an egg is fertilizable vary from five to forty-eight hours, it can probably be assumed that each time the woman ovulates (that is, produces an egg) she can probably get pregnant over a period of not more than twenty hours. If we assume that the average woman ovulates only ten times a year, it becomes apparent that there are less than ten days in the course of a year during which time a woman can get pregnant. This, by the way, is considered a second proof that man is a relatively infertile animal.

One of the best ways of correlating the female's internal reproductive organs is menstruation. Menstruation is the monthly preparation for pregnancy. If pregnancy does not take place, the woman menstruates. If pregnancy does take place, she does not menstruate. She may, in the course of pregnancy, bleed from any number of causes, but in no sense can she really be said to be menstruating. If a woman starts to menstruate on January 1, what she actually is doing is getting rid of a lining that was built up in her womb during the month of December. Now nature does nothing in a static fashion. Nature never just builds up or tears down; she always does both at the same time, so at the very time that nature is getting rid of the lining which was not used in December she begins to build a new lining for the womb for January. As an approximation, for say, the first two weeks of January, in the average (textbook) woman, the womb becomes a beehive of activity wherein a soft, foam-like mattress is set up in its lining. This is soft and velvety and with every justification can be considered a bed. Once the egg is produced (*pretty nearly* at mid cycle), this soft, foamy mattress contains a nourishing fluid so that in case of pregnancy there is nourishment for the growing embryo. If pregnancy does not take place, then about eight days after the egg has been produced, the lining of the womb dies, since there is no need for it, and four days later the woman is said to menstruate.

So, the function of menstruation is the sloughing out of a lining of the womb that was not used for a pregnancy. Most of the menstrual flow is the dead lining of the womb. In addition there are the tissue juices which have been placed there as a nourishing element in case a pregnancy should take place. All of this is stained by a small quantity of blood, and blood, being a powerful stain, causes all of the material to look like blood. Actually, there is comparatively little blood passed in the course of the average menstrual period; the general estimate is one to four ounces of blood in a five- to seven-day flow. Perhaps the best definition of menstruation is the statement that "Menstruation is the weeping of a disappointed womb." This implies that the cycle of menstruation is a monthly preparation for pregnancy, and when pregnancy does not take place, the womb weeps for sheer disappointment.

If the pregnancy does occur, then the egg moves down to the lining of the womb and there impregnates itself. Actually, sperm are deposited at the neck of the womb, and since the sperm have tails, the sperm can swim at a rate of about one inch every eight minutes from the neck of the womb up into the tube where one of them commonly meets the egg in pregnancy. To cover this distance takes about thirty minutes. If approximately 400,000,000 sperm are deposited at the neck of the womb, about 30,000 actually get to the tube, but only one ever penetrates the egg. The egg, on the other hand, being one of the biggest cells in the human body is a slow, lumbering, clumsy structure which is produced by the ovary about halfway between the periods, or perhaps more accurately, closer to two weeks before the next expected period. The egg, having been picked up by the tube, is siphoned into the tube and begins its slow, clumsy way down to the womb itself. This voyage from the ovary to the womb ordinarily takes eight to twelve days. Impregnation actually occurs in the tube, and when the egg is fertilized, if the tube is normal, the egg gradually moves down the tube into the womb, where it finds a soft, spongy, foamy bed filled with a nourishing fluid. By this time, the fertilized egg is capable of burrowing into the bed and building a home for itself, for the next nine months.

Functions of the Husband in the Act of Love in Marriage

The male's reaction to the act of love is an instantaneous one. This means that the mere proximity of the person he loves may be sufficient to excite him to the point where he is in the state of erection; that is, where his penis becomes large, hard, and erect. Under these conditions, a man is said to be sexually excited and ready to perform the marital act. The fact that this reaction is an instantaneous one is no sign of masculine ability or unusual prowess. It is simply the way the male is built. Occasionally, under conditions of unusual fatigue, emotional strain, or during convalescence from an illness, the man may not be able to function in this way, and the woman may have to actively stimulate him to arouse him to a point of sexual excitement. This she commonly does by fondling his sexual organs and particularly the tip of the penis itself.

Equally important regarding the male's sexual reaction is the fact that though his function is almost instantaneous, he has the ability, or may easily acquire it, after a few days of marriage, to hold off, even though he is in the state of erection, from the marital act until his wife is also ready. For the first few days, or the first week or two of marriage, as we have already indicated, because of the tension involved in the first attempts in the marriage act, the husband may not be able to hold off from ejaculating his sperm until he is able to penetrate his wife's body, let alone wait until she is completely ready for the performance of the act. However, within a very short time the husband usually acquires this ability, and as the tension is reduced and the couple learn to know one another better and to love one another better, adjusting to the marital act becomes easier. His wife, therefore, does him no injustice, under ordinary circumstances, in requiring him to wait until she is also ready once they have become acclimated to the love act itself. On the contrary, under most conditions and with most people, the husband has some obligation to wait until his wife is also ready, even though he is in the state of erection, so both may receive almost simultaneously in the marital act the normal pleasure which is their right, due, and heritage as individuals. Actually, it is not important, for most people, to experience the orgasm or complete sexual pleasure, simultaneously. What is important is the realization that when the act is performed, both partners are entitled to the normal pleasure that a kind God has ordained for them.

For some couples, it is the normal, usual custom to sexually stimulate the wife to the point where she has her full satisfaction prior to the act. This is permissible provided the normally performed marital act follows. With other couples, the wife gets her complete satisfaction after the performance of the act, her husband providing the stimulation manually. Again it is perfectly permissible for the wife to get her complete satisfaction this way, provided that the act be performed. The husband, of course, gets his complete satisfaction from the marital act itself. Ideally, it would be best if both partners could achieve their full sexual pleasure, as God has ordained, simultaneously. But the important thing to remember is that this is an ideal situation; it is not abnormal if the sexual pleasure of both must be satisfied prior to or following the act, provided the act is performed.

Rather rarely at the beginning of a marriage a husband finds it difficult or is unable to have an erection. In most cases this is psychological and rather easily corrected. In a few instances, the basis is some organic difficulty, but here again assistance can be given to most men. Should a difficulty in erection occur, the husband should promptly seek advice so tension does not build up fruitlessly over a minor issue that can be corrected fairly quickly.

Functions of the Wife in the Act of Love in Marriage

The female reaction to the act of love in marriage is not instantaneous. It is important to remember this. The average woman requires a period of love-making, a period of sexual stimulation, because she is a woman, normal, married, and in love with her husband. In love-making, in addition to the normal kissing and caressing of her breasts, the wife's clitoris and vagina are stimulated by her husband's hands from twenty to thirty-five minutes prior to the act itself. The fact that a woman requires this length of time for sexual stimulation to the act itself does not mean that she is a freak, nor that she doesn't love her husband, nor that he doesn't love her, nor that they are subconsciously unsuited for marriage, nor that they really hate one another, nor that she is frigid, nor that he is predatory, nor any other silly reason so commonly found in popular journals and writings on this subject. A woman is slow to be stimulated and requires a long period of love-making because this is the normal reaction which God intended her to have so she might achieve from the act of love in marriage her right, due, and heritage. And we repeat, the male has the ability (or may easily acquire it in most instances) to remain in the state of erection at no injustice to him until his wife is also ready.

The average woman (again it must be remembered she is

generally found in textbooks) may be married for as long as six weeks to six months before she gets from the act of love the complete satisfaction which is generally referred to as "coming off" or orgasm. This seems to contradict what has been written above. We said that the husband, if possible, should wait until his wife is also ready, that he has some obligation to her as her lover to stimulate her for a sufficient length of time prior to the act of love so that she may get from the act the normal pleasure which is her right. Now we say that the average girl may be married for as long as six weeks to six months before she experiences full, complete sexual pleasure. The explanation of this apparent contradiction is very simple. It takes some couples, because of disparity of size or anatomical differences, six weeks to six months to learn to know one another's bodies well enough to love one another properly. If the wife is not getting full satisfaction at the end of six months or six weeks, or even two weeks, if there is a strain on the family tie, then the *couple,* not the wife, should seek advice to find out what they are doing that is cheating her of her heritage.

The question is frequently asked, What is the nature of orgasm and how may it be defined or described? One of the amazing features of orgasm or complete sexual satisfaction and pleasure is that as often as it has occurred to people in love since the beginning of time, no one has ever adequately or accurately defined it. In the husband, there is a succession of rhythmic movements reached at the peak of emotional excitement and associated with the ejaculation in a spurting fashion of the seminal fluid as it is deposited in his wife's vagina. This physical function is associated with reaching a peak of physical, emotional, spiritual, and psychological stimulation which is rather short-lived and somewhat fatiguing, but leaves the husband with an extreme sense of tranquility and relaxation.

So far as the wife is concerned, description is even more difficult. The wife's reaction is much slower and requires stimulation by the husband acting as her lover by kissing, caressing, caressing and rubbing the breasts, rubbing certain erogenous areas in the body such as the neck and the skin of the inner thigh, and manually stimulating the vulva, the lips of the front passage, the clitoris, the urethra, and the tissues about the urethra. This is done over a period of time as long as thirty-five minutes, during which the wife becomes more and more sexually excited and restless physically and emotionally—so much so that her initial orgasm may actually frighten her. Many attempts have been made to have women describe or define the sensation. Perhaps the best definition came from a woman who described the building of sexual excitement and orgasm as being not unlike the explosions of a Roman candle. When a Roman candle is lit the material reaches high into the sky, culminating in an explosion and leaving a lazy, relaxed shower of stars. This is generally repeated several times in one candle. Similarly, it is not uncommon for the woman to have more than one orgasm in the course of one intercourse. Again, the act is physically tiring, and when properly completed leaves a woman with a sense of peace and relaxation and tranquillity which pervades the personality. The effects in the wife are profoundly physical, emotional, psychological, and spiritual, and of much longer duration than in the husband. The keen sense of satisfaction obtained by the wife is frequently described as being a glow that lasts upwards of one hour.

From a physical point of view, the act of love in marriage and the orgasm associated with it is not related in the female to the ejaculation of any secretion other than the lubricating secretion mentioned several times previously. However, there may be rhythmic motions which complement the rhythmic motions of the husband just as he enters into orgasm and is ejaculating his sperm, especially if both experience their complete satisfaction simultaneously. When a woman has orgasm apart from the simultaneous expression of love with her husband, she experiences a building tension and an explosion point, which is followed quite suddenly by a state of sleepy relaxation, an experience discernible to both the woman and her husband.

Dangerous Misconceptions about the Act of Love in Marriage

The marital act is plagued by popular misconceptions and even vicious misrepresentations. These old wives' tales, as they are called, seem to be set up with woman as the target. There are three times in a woman's life when other women are apt to be cruel to her. The first time is just before she gets married; the second time is just before she has her first baby (after she has had one child, it is pretty difficult for the "local crew" to pull the wool over her eyes); and the third time is apt to be either on the occasion of a "female operation" or at the change of life. On such occasions, there seems to be a universal herd of women who, like termites, come out of the very walls themselves possessed with an obsession that it is their inborn privilege and duty to get the information "down to the troops." These misguided souls possess unusual imaginations and an almost Messianic zeal; as soon as a girl has that naked, glittering engagement ring on her finger, unprotected by the single gold wedding band, she becomes their immediate prey.

Who are these harpies? Unfortunately, they may be members of the woman's own family, a neighbor, a woman who sits in the next seat of the trolley car, someone at the next desk in the office—almost anyone who has a tongue longer than charity allows.

Their stories have many variations, but they generally are based upon two main themes. The first is, "This business is messy, and you won't like it any more than I did." They are referring, of course, to the marital act, and by messy they mean the natural secretions which are produced by both partners. As previously indicated, the spermatic fluid produced by the male is about a teaspoonful in quantity. The largest secretion of lubricating fluid is produced by the female. These secretions naturally bathe the reproductive organs of both partners in the marital act of love. They are normal secretions, and under usual circumstances they require only some tissue by the bedside for immediate cleanliness. The only further care that is needed is the normal, external cleanliness generally afforded by the morning bath or shower.

But the way in which this story is related, the distasteful look on the person's face as it is told, leads a young bride-to-be to believe that she is about to encounter an animalistic and dirty process. In the end it boils down to the old couplet, "Two men looked out from prison bars—the one saw mud and the other saw stars." In other words, it depends upon the point of view. If people want to go through life looking for mud, they will be enormously successful. "Mud" is universal and can be found in quantities sufficient for humans to wallow in it. To seek it is a peculiar choice. Those who so elect, never grow tall in life and miss the symbolism at least of blue skies and the reminders of Heaven. If they prefer to look upon the sublime act by which they are able to love one another and to produce a personal pleasure granted by God Himself as being associated with mud, with the gross, the mundane, and the crudely biological—then I think all of us, collectively, feel sorry for them, and they are deserving of our prayers. If, on the other hand, they believe in looking at stars, if they believe that marriages are born in heaven, if they believe that the beauty found in the ability to give to and to love someone else here on earth and to share their happiness is something that is a God-given gift and a personal reward from God to man, then I think the average, well-thinking couple and, certainly, the average, well-thinking woman can be dissuaded from the concept given to her by these unfortunately misguided creatures.

As a corollary to this, many women will tell a woman about to be married that she should take a douche after the marriage act has been performed. There are several points to be made here.

No douche should be taken for any reason for at least thirty minutes after intercourse. In the past, douches have been recommended in certain circles as a means of contraception. This advice is no longer being given with any serious thought because it is the poorest possible method of contraception. However, more important are the esthetics of the whole situation. No girl, after having been properly loved, should have the slightest inclination to get out of bed and do anything, let alone take a douche. The act of love in marriage is a physically tiring function. Psychologically, it is very soothing, and both partners should be left with a sense of peace with God, themselves, and the world, with a sublime sense of contentment so that they should want only to get together as close as possible and go to sleep. Any girl who becomes so obsessed with such a grossly mundane affair as taking an unnecessary douche under these conditions is in all probability someone whom love is passing by.

The second statement which these alleged and self-appointed advisers are apt to preach to a woman is another old saw which reads, "A woman's only part in the marital act is a duty to the old man." This statement is not only steeped in ignorance but actually represents a vilification of man, and in addition, seeks to place woman as a mere object for the pleasure of man. Such a statement denies the very nature of love; it denies that love requires two people, one to do the loving and the other to be loved, and the act to be mutual. Such a statement denies that happiness was born a twin; it denies that marriage is a contract which, binding in justice and love, requires the fulfillment of pleasure of two people, man and woman, one giving pleasure to the other and each to the other. It further denies the nature of woman. It denies that there are placed in women by a kind God organs which, when properly stimulated and reacting properly, will offer to her the same pleasure, perhaps even longer-lasting and perhaps even to a higher degree of intensity, as that which man experiences.

However much we may decry the statements made by these unhappy advisers, and however much we may be disturbed by the effect that these statements have on girls who otherwise might enjoy a greater degree of happiness, we must, in all charity, consider the fact that these people are probably speaking from personal frustrations. We must recognize that they are probably the victims of unhappy, personal experiences, that they may have been so unfortunate as to have been married to an incompetent lover or to an inconsiderate person, or perhaps even more tragic, they may have some quirk in their own natures which will not allow them to let their husbands love them.

The statement is made not uncommonly that women tend to be unresponsive. Some authorities say that 40 per cent of all women do not appreciate fully the love act or that most women do not derive any pleasure upwards of 60 per cent of the time. There is an important distinction to be made here. Too many people confuse the unarousable female with the unaroused woman. The former is rare and usually quite ill from the point of view of emotional hygiene. The latter is in need of knowledge sometimes (more often perhaps it is her husband that requires education), the gentle approach, some help in correcting an attitude—but more than anything else a husband who is loving, competent, and potent.

In defense of woman, let it be said that due to fatigue, tension, illness, or anxiety, the desire for conjugal love may at any time be low or absent *in either partner*. Many wives show an awareness of this that is not reflected in the expert opinions. They also are considerate of their husband's fatigue, or tension. On the other hand, it is too commonly true that men are apt to be unthinking and unaware of their wives' moods or daily difficulties. This means that they are also unaware that their attitude and approach to the act of love is a measure of their abilities as lovers and can be all-important in the woman's response and proper arousal.

At the same time, it is true that some women are brought up to feel that it is unladylike for them to let their husbands know when the desire is great. The point of this whole problem is that in the maturation and acclimatization of a genuine love the couple soon learn to recognize each other's emotional state and needs, and the proper fruition of such matings does lead to the satisfaction intended by the Lord in a high percentage of cases.

Physicians, by nature of their calling, must be realistic. Any physician speaking realistically about marriage must, of necessity, speak realistically about love. The experience not only of physicians but of divorce court lawyers, probate court judges, social workers, clergymen, marriage counselors, and people who have to deal with marriage and its problems come realistically to one conclusion: the marriage which is cemented by genuine love and the ability of individuals to give to one another, the marriage wherein the partners are seeking always to find out what they can do for each other, the marriage which represents a genuine mutual selection as an avenue of salvation—is the marriage that, however rough the wind and the storm, can always reach port. On the other hand, the marriage which is predicated upon advantage or selfishness will never reach home.

For every couple entering marriage there is always a festival, a marriage feast, an exchange of gifts. The gifts that are spread for the admiration of the guests are something tangible, and they are perpetuated in the American slang as "the loot" to be guarded on the wedding day. Among such is never the most precious gift and possession of a couple who are truly in love. The best wedding gift that any couple can achieve on their wedding day is the blessing of the gift of giving. The extent of their ability to give to one another for better or worse, till death do them part, will define most properly their success in marriage. Any couple whose members are blessed with a gift of giving to one another will therein find real joy, and their greatest happiness will be found in giving to those that God gives to them. Neither the climate, nor the heat, nor the station in life, nor the economics of life's situation, nor the fluctuations of Wall Street, nor the size of the house, nor the plot of land can have any effect on this most precious and God-given gift. All of these things are secondary in a couple's possession of one another in the Face of God, and their ability to give to each other, not only themselves but salvation as well. Happiness, heaven-sent, indeed is born a twin.

9

Limitation of the Family

The problem of family limitation has become clearly defined only recently. In past eras of history, on a more or less local basis, a time of famine caused grave concern to individuals lest their family grow larger and there be more mouths to feed on short rations. On the other hand, trail-blazing pioneers have usually sought large families to increase population and the number of hands willing to challenge nature. Various military states at various times in history, and even within our own times, have urged large families as a means of building up economic and military strength; however, the size of the family has been usually an individual choice.

Within the last century, it has been obvious to serious students of social and political science that as the world has become larger it has, at the same time, grown smaller. With mass methods of communication, one man may influence millions. Events in an individual city may have a nationwide impact. Problems, even population problems, of geographically small nations have had world-wide influence. The actions of almost any country now influence for good or for evil the entire world.

Recently, our attention has been focused upon what has been called the population explosion, the dangers of overpopulation of the world. This is a captivating subject, and serious attempts are being made to point out to peoples throughout the world their national responsibility in this area. Furthermore, a concerted effort is being made to teach individual responsibility for family-planning, as it is called, since populations grow at the family level.

The world is changing in many respects. As education is brought to more and more people, the importance of the educative function of parents is being emphasized as never before. To nations, the importance of an educated and informed people, at least within the democratic community, has become a major concern of government. The economics of nations are in the process of change, and there is no Solomon to predict which government is going to alter its economy in which fashion in any period of time. The demands made upon a nation's economy simply by the achievements of modern medical science in increasing the average length of life is almost incalculable—and it is a foregone conclusion that these demands will increase in the future. Therefore, on a personal basis, an individual family must make a decision, with whatever wisdom is at their command, regarding the number of children they can, with fairness, bring into the world and educate properly, bearing in mind the kind of world in which they live and its current problems.

The population of the world seems destined to double or triple itself by the year 2000. There is cause for real concern. Not only Malthusians but other serious socially-minded people fear the world may not be able to feed itself by then if this trend continues.

As simply an aside to this problem, and stated without prejudice, it might be pointed out that we always hear about the semi-miraculous steps that have been taken by science in so many fields of endeavor; the gloomy outlook seems to be limited to the ability of science to find a means of feeding a growing population. By some mystique, the same scientists who have developed an atomic bomb, automation, vehicles to throw a man into space and bring him back, and the tools and instruments by which man eventually will be guided to the moon and back, are judged incapable of finding sources of food supply to take care of the expanding world population.

Nevertheless, the recent campaign to focus attention on the overpopulation problem is justified. The expanding world population is one of the facts of life that must be faced in the modern world. It is a problem which is real to the point of tragedy in some parts of a still-underdeveloped world. The problem of the expanding population of the world is a challenge to every group, social, political, and religious. And it is a challenge which must be accepted at the individual level, too.

The Moral Considerations of Contraception

Unhappily, the impression has been left with too many people that the problem of over-population and the problem of contraception are so closely intertwined that when one is satisfactorily answered the other will be at the same time. This view is too narrow and incomplete. It is obvious from their writings and speeches that the people who favor contraception, particularly those who favor the contraceptive pills, such as the progestins which are capable of suspending ovulation (the production of an egg) in a woman for a predicted period of time, are vitally concerned with the overpopulation problem. But if anyone studies the problem of contraception for very long, delves deeply into its history, or properly evaluates its limitations, one finds it is merely one facet of a many-sided problem.

The real issue is one of *a* standard of morality versus *multiple* standards of morality which may fluctuate in countries, individuals, or eras. One cannot face the issue of contraception alone for very long. Closely associated with contraception, especially for purposes of population control, is the problem of sterilization, compulsory or voluntary. Closely allied with this is sterilization of the unfit for eugenic reasons supposedly to produce a population which is not only limited but better. To those who enthusiastically embrace mass or individual contraception, it is merely a temporary measure— the next logical step is sterilization: "If contraception is good, sterilization is better." Abortion must also be considered in this moral picture because the logic of the new thinkers insists that if contraception or sterilization fails, you resort to abortion. No one really feels that abortion is an effective means of population control; nevertheless, it is practiced in Japan by the millions each year as a partial answer to the population program there. Interestingly enough, those who preach abortion for population reasons generally urge abortion as a means of extricating people from difficult economic or social situations.

As each facet of what may be called the "social problems" of reproduction are investigated, it is striking to note that human life seems less and less inviolate and more and more expendable. Thus euthanasia is recommended to eliminate those who, as the Nazis would have it, are drains on society or to "mercifully" put to death people incurably ill who, therefore, are also drains on their families' emotions and savings or on society.

Artificial insemination is the last bed-fellow of the group because those who feel that population should be controlled quantitatively feel that it should be controlled qualitatively also. We are repeatedly exhorted to profit by the lessons of animal husbandry and learn to "breed better people." In recent years, a group of doctors and socially-minded scientists has tried to stimulate the interest of the legal profession to formulate a set of laws which would cover problems from contraception to artificial insemination. Such a code of laws would be offered to all fifty states through their legislative bodies in an attempt to legislate a uniform code of laws broadening the instance where these practices are now permitted and permitting such practices where now forbidden.

A philosophy is being developed along a concept known as the Fifth Freedom. The Fifth Freedom presumes that man in his evolution has now reached the stage in which he has, or should have, the freedom of choice to do with himself, his life, and his procreative capacity (that is, family) whatever he chooses. It is pointed out by the protagonists of such a concept that as the population is controlled the quality of the population should be controlled. They further insist that if the East and West are to successfully live in peace with one another a new level of human being must be developed to solve our complex problems. Breeding by artificial insemination along the lines of animal husbandry is offered as the means of manufacturing the new family and the new human.

Within the next generation, or certainly within fifty years, we will see not only the effects, good and bad, of an almost unimaginable progress in science; we will see also the effects on the communities of the world of an ever more definite line dividing the world into two camps on a philosophical-theological basis.

On the one hand will stand those who believe there is no *standard* of morality, only *standards* of morality which change for eras, circumstances, "situations," and people; that the present systems of philosophy and religion were valid in their day and doubtless served a good purpose, but they are outmoded and antiquated; that religion is so much dogmatic mysticism; that the family as a unit of society is a social convenience; that paternal pride is sentimentalism; and that the sanctity of life, at least in some aspects of living, is overly exaggerated by a naive group of people who choose not to face the realities of a cold-war world.

Opposing them will be those who believe that a standard of morality arising from their Creator should govern the actions of those whom He has created; that when God created man He created him with the expectation that man would return to Him; that marriage is more than a social unit, that it is a means of salvation, a means of producing new life that also may be sent back to God; that there is legitimate pride in being a father and glory in becoming a mother; that it is wrong to kill another human being or to steal someone else's property; that the Ten Commandments are here to stay; that the family is the unit in which people live creatively, productively, and that it is an institution in which others, as they come along, may be taught to live according to a revealed plan of God.

It is obvious then that the "simple" problem of family limitation has very broad connotations. It is also obvious that there is a strong moral issue involved in family limitation which goes well beyond the mere problem of contraception with which it is generally equated in our society. Family limitation, however, at the personal level, has its own particular medical and moral problems. The issue here is clear, it is contraception versus periodic continence.

Contraceptive Devices: Contrary to Natural Law

Contraception, or positive contraception, or positive birth control, as it is variously known, involves the use of some mechanical aid, chemical adjuvant, or hormone which singly or together interfere with the proper completion of the marital act or prevent the development of the egg in the female. In this latter connection, it might be pointed out that considerable work has been done on a non-hormonal pill which will suppress the development of sperm in the male. As of this writing, it has not yet appeared on the commercial market. So far as the morality of the chemical and mechanical means of preventing conception are concerned, the matter is comparatively simple. As creatures we are dependent upon God. However, God created us to be rational creatures with intellect, reason, and will, with an ability to know the difference between right and wrong and to follow the plan that He devised. We serve God when we follow His plan. In recognizing God as the author of life, we also recognize that life and the means for life are His domain, and we have been given these to hold in trust. When we enter into marriage, we hold the means for life, with His cooperation, in the marital act. Since we hold this function only in trust for God, we cannot interfere in the marital act in any way that will frustrate its completion or interfere with His plan.

Since diaphragms and other mechanical gadgets, withdrawal by the male before the act is completed, and chemical contraceptive agents interfere with the properly performed act of love in marriage, which intends the union of the sperm with the egg, these actions are contrary to the nature of the act and contrary to the nature of God's plan or the natural law and are, therefore, immoral or sinful.

People who have no moral compunctions on the use of

contraceptives often object to them on other grounds. For example, the use of contraceptives develops an attitude which involves a deliberate attempt to avoid fulfillment of the contract of marriage; and if the habit of avoidance of responsibilities in marriage occurs in this, the major field of the marriage contract, it will also flow out to other aspects of marriage. Furthermore, a deliberate attempt to prevent pregnancy makes pregnancy, instead of being the fruit of the love between two people, seem distasteful and to be assiduously avoided. People who use contraceptives generally are determined not to fail, and should they fail, either the child born of that pregnancy is not welcome or it is a simple matter for them to step to the next lower rung in the ladder and to seek an abortion. People who feel no qualms about breaking the contract of marriage itself, generally give little thought to the idea that the unborn life of a child is inviolate.

Many women, particularly, object to the use of contraceptives as being unesthetic. The spontaneity of the love-act in marriage is lost, and love must be made by a "gadget." They feel, furthermore, that the onus of contraception is generally laid upon the woman inasmuch as the male type of contraceptive is distasteful to the male and he is usually unwilling to use it. No form of contraceptive device has any esthetic appeal, to say the least. People who use them seem to have an innate distaste for them and eventually conclude that the use of a contraceptive device or chemical actually divorces sex from marriage. Because of the nature of humans the use of a contraceptive device is at best unpalatable.

Contraceptive Pills: Contrary to Natural Law

With the possible exception of polio and its attendant vaccines, the progestin contraceptive pill has commanded more space among the news media in the last half-century than any other medical subject. This is probably due to the efforts of one of the better-known advertising agencies in the country and the natural controversial nature of the subject itself. To put the matter very simply the progestin pill is a hormone which will prevent ovulation when taken by the female according to a prescribed dosage and schedule. It differs from other pills, which have been available for many years, that also prevent ovulation in that it is far more powerful than anything that has been available to medicine up to now. Furthermore, it can be taken almost indefinitely and if taken properly, will prevent ovulation indefinitely. The cost of the pill is now within reasonable limits, at least for an American public, and there seems little reason to doubt its effectiveness as a contraceptive. But from a medical point of view, there are still unsolved problems and unanswered questions. Here are some of them:

1. In a considerable percentage of women, the pills tend to produce some of the undesirable symptoms of pregnancy—nausea, swelling of the breasts, fatigue, swelling of the feet and abdomen, weight gain, and irritability. Women sometimes complain that they have all the symptoms of pregnancy without pregnancy itself.

2. Periodically, women may have slight bleeding or staining in the course of the treatment with the drug. This is break-through bleeding and requires additional use of the drug to control. To some women this is upsetting and annoying.

3. Not a few women complain that they lose all appetite for the love-act in marriage and complain that sexually they feel like "a thing."

4. The long-range effects over a period of years are not yet known. There are still many gynecologists who have

no compunction morally about their use as contraceptives who will not use them on women under the age of forty-five. Others restrict the use of the pill to not more than one year. The danger lies in the possible effects upon the ovary at a later date. Changes have been noticed in the ovary after the use of the drug for some time which are very similar, if not identical, to changes found in ovaries of women who have been subject to malnutrition for long periods of time, or women who have had radiation of their ovaries. In the patient getting the contraceptive pill, these changes are apparently reversible, but their significance is not yet understood. Their breast effect is almost unknown.

5. Since ovulation is suppressed by the drug, experts wonder if this ovulation process is held in a state of suspended animation, so to speak. When the contraceptive effect of the pill has worn off, will the ovary continue to produce eggs well beyond the years in which the woman would normally have stopped producing eggs? There is serious concern that a woman who has been taking the drug for an extended period may continue to ovulate as late as the age of sixty. In this regard it is interesting to note that in Massachusetts alone in the last twenty years, twenty women beyond the age of fifty have borne live babies.

6. If some "pills" are given inadvertently in an early pregnancy they are definitely capable of producing masculinity in female fetuses. And this is always possible; in Puerto Rico, 1.5 per cent of patients on the pills were subsequently found to have been pregnant.

7. The possible relationship of phlebitis to the contraceptive pill is still far from settled and it would be unfair to draw any conclusions at this time.

8. One final problem. These pills can be used for purposes

other than contraception. They may be used in a number of gynecological situations in which there is malfunction or disease of the female reproductive organs. Here, their intended use is to correct the malfunction or as the first step in a projected program of therapy for a particular disease. In this regard, it has been widely stated that the hormone may be used to regulate the periods of a woman who has been previously quite irregular. By irregular we mean that her monthly menstrual pattern varies ten days or more over the course of a calendar year. While it is true that a woman who is on the progestin-type pill will have regular bleeding, depending on the schedule which she is following, it is significant—and it should be remembered—that while she is on the pill she is not menstruating in the true sense but is having *false periods* produced by the hormone. These false periods actually represent a form of anovulatory bleeding, called *withdrawal bleeding*, which means that the bleeding comes from the effects of the hormone and is not associated with the production of an egg. The egg, as a matter of fact, has been suppressed during each one of the "menstrual cycles" or bleeding episodes which occur when the drug is withdrawn. When this is done for a period of a few months in an attempt to "prime the pump," it is a legitimate form of therapy. The idea here is that when the drug has been stopped after a period of a few months, the woman will hopefully then pick up a normal, regular pattern herself. In the history of hormones such treatment has always been used but without notable success.

Recently work has been initiated on drugs which will control ovulation—that is, will so function as to produce ovulation on a given predicted date. Such a drug offers much hope that we are getting closer to a moral answer to the problems of overpopulation, provided the drug—any drug—hormonal or otherwise, can be proven to be safe.

Thus if by chance a hormone is isolated that can predictably control ovulation some minimal proof of the following will be necessary:

1. The drug does no harm—even on long-term use.

2. In controlling ovulation it would have to be shown to safeguard the health and integrity of the egg which it is summoning somewhat off schedule. This is of great importance because it would be an assurance of normalcy of any pregnancy that might arise from such an egg when fertilized.

But as one British authority (Dodds) put it, "It may be dangerous to interfere with rhythmical processes, and even if you thoroughly understand the mechanism of a clock, if it is going well it should be left alone, for interference with its mechanism can be disastrous." So if a woman is ovulating, whether her periods are *regular* or *not*, it is generally conceded from a purely medical point of view to be better medicine not to interfere with delicate mechanisms. One can't cheat nature with impunity.

A drug known as di-acetyl diamid, an amebicide, has been used on a research basis with a group of male volunteers in an effort to develop a male contraceptive pill. The preliminary reports indicate that when taken according to the prescribed dosage the sperm count of the male goes from normal to zero in sixty days. So long as the drug is maintained the sperm count remains zero and the testicles become somewhat smaller and soft. As soon as the drug is removed, the testicles regain their usual tone and size and within sixty days a normal sperm count results. The drug is not a hormone and to date seems to have no apparent ill effects nor side reactions. The difficulties involved are three:

1. The sperm count drops gradually in a course of sixty days, and during that sixty-day period numerous abnormal forms of sperm are seen. Similarly, once the drug is stopped, as the sperm count regenerates to normal, numerous abnormal sperm are also seen. The danger is that should conception occur within these first or last sixty days, an abnormal pregnancy *might* result.
2. There is also grave doubt that the male would use such a pill. There is some considerable doubt that from a psychological point of view the male would use a drug which he *knew* would make him absolutely incapable of becoming a father.
3. From a moral point of view di-acetyl is forbidden, of course, since it interferes with the properly performed marital act.

A third drug, the anti-nidation pill, still in its investigative stage, is a drug which does not interfere with production of either the egg or sperm. It represents a chemical abortifacient. This drug acts to prevent the fertilized egg from implanting itself in the womb. Thus, the conceptus dies of lack of nutrition in a matter of days after fertilization.

Every new drug or therapeutic technique which arrives on the medical scene is viewed with cautious enthusiasm. The *enthusiasm* varies with the need for the therapy—for any new treatment for a disease such as multiple sclerosis, for which there presently is no known treatment, enthusiasm would be great; but another treatment for pneumonia would inspire prolonged discussion of many aspects, including a comparison with drugs in present use.

The *caution*, however, is always with us. Medicine has too often enthusiastically greeted a new drug in terms of what it does for the patient, only to learn bitterly that it usually takes considerably longer to discover what the drug will do *to* the patient. This is a truth the validity of which must constantly be brought to the attention of enthusiasts in medicine, the lay press, and the public.

We simply do not have the last word on the medical aspects of any oral preparation for contraception now available, and we will not have it for some time. Any new product will have to stand the test of time, particularly since the organs involved are delicate and sensitive to medication and hormones, and any effects on them can possibly be transmitted to the next generation.

We hear that the new pills represent a threat of malignancy; that malignancy of the body of the womb *seems* to be lessened; that cancer of the breast and cervix (neck of the womb) may be increased. These statements involve series of cases so small as to be negligible but at least inconclusive. Any conclusions on these aspects would at this time be arbitrary and unreliable.

The morality of such drugs is similar to the morality of the other contraceptive agents. All contraceptive pills, male and female types, interfere with the properly performed marriage act—which act intends the union of the sperm with the egg— and are, therefore, immoral and sinful.

The anti-nidation pill interferes with the nutrition (and hence the life) of the conceptus just as deliberately and effectively (apparently) as the abortionist's curette and is, therefore, an intended, if chemical, abortion.

Other types of contraceptive pills are emerging on the medical horizon. That some method satisfactory to all will emerge in the next decade seems reasonable. From the Catholic point of view, in keeping with the natural law and the intended purposes of marriage and the marriage act, such a method will have to satisfy certain fundamental conditions:

1. A reliable method for detecting ovulation *at the time* of *ovulation.*

2. A method of regulating menstruation without interfering with ovulation. This probably will entail a method which will involve some method of initiating or controlling the time of ovulation without interfering with the process itself.

3. The method, whatever its nature, must be medically proven to be safe over an extended and extensive experience in harmony with the fundamental premise of good medicine—"Primum Non Nocere."

It is interesting that more than thirty years ago Pius XI in his Encyclical on Christian Marriage seemed to anticipate the new drugs. "Any use whatsoever of matrimony exercised in such a way that the act is deliberately frustrated in its natural power to generate life is an offense against the law of God and of nature, and those who indulge in such are branded with the guilt of grave sin. . . . Since, therefore, the conjugal act is destined primarily by nature for the begetting of children, those who in exercising it deliberately frustrate its natural power and purpose, sin against nature and commit a deed which is shameful and intrinsically evil."

The Use of Periodic Continence

The whole problem of family limitation, as previously pointed out, is a relatively new one. It wasn't so very long ago when the people that we knew were proud of the fact that they had five, eight, ten, or twelve children. A large family was considered a blessing, a source of envy, and the small family was looked upon as a tragedy and sometimes as a sign of selfishness. Catholic thinking has always been that parents enjoyed the privilege of cooperating with God to bring new life into the world and that children were a special blessing to their lives. The beauty of the family and family life has always been singled out for special attention and praise, but there has never been any encouragement, dicta, or exhortation for people to have as many children as they could possibly have. The number of children for an individual couple has always been based upon the ability of the couple to bring them into the world, rear them according to Christian principles, and educate them properly.

Interestingly enough, in this regard, Pius XII gave two famous allocutions in a single calendar year. In the first, talking to an association of large families of Italy, he gave special praise in his blessing to large families: "The Christian spirit of love watches over the family's order and tranquillity while it dispenses almost drawing upon nature itself, the intimate family joys common to parents, children, and brothers—but God also visits large families with His Providence, to which the parents, especially poor ones, give an open testimony by placing in it their entire trust when human efforts are not sufficient. It is a trust well founded and not in vain. . . . God does not deny the means to live to those He calls to life."

The second allocution was the address to the Italian Catholic Union of Midwives, October 29, 1951. This is famous because it is the first formulated, authoritative statement by the Church on the problem of family limitation. There was not, and is not now, any consideration that this represented a change in the Church's thinking. It is simply a fact that no formulated, authoritative statement ever had been made on the subject before.

Actually, the Church's teaching on this whole problem is quite clear. Marriage is a vocation and a means of salvation for the two partners involved in the contract. It is a contract wherein the partners give the rights to the reproductive organs to each other. It is a means of establishing society by establishing the family as the unit of society. The Holy Father pointed out that the individual, society, the Church, and the state, depend for their existence on fertile marriage. Therefore, he stated quite clearly that

1. Married people have an obligation to have children as their duty to the human race.
2. The obligation can be excused for good reason. He summarized these reasons as being medical, eugenic, social, and economic; these will be discussed further below.
3. Even though the couple agree or have substantiated by good judgment for them that they have good reason for family limitation, there must be mutual consent, freely given, on the part of both to so use their procreative powers that they will limit the size of their family. In other words, that they will use periodic continence.
4. Regardless of the good reasons that they may have for using periodic continence, it can be further used only if both members are capable of using it. In other words, if to keep an agreement to abstain from sexual relations during the fertile period would so tax the sexual urge and needs of either member of the partnership and would tempt them to masturbation or to seek solace outside of marriage, then periodic continence could not be used.
5. In the event that periodic continence fails and pregnancy supervenes, the couple must be in agreement that such a pregnancy will be welcome and not rejected.

There is a distinct difference between contraception and family limitation. To many non-Catholics this distinction seems specious. They feel that since the Church agrees to the

basic premise that family limitation under certain circumstances is licit, to make an issue about the methods employed
is a little silly. They feel that they have a twofold duty,
one to have children and second to control the number of
children which they have. They feel that it is unnatural to
abstain from sexual relations for any prolonged period of
time because the strain this might put on the marriage tie
could also be morally wrong. They feel that it is why you do
something and not what you do that makes the difference
between a good or bad act.

Our belief is that the marital act is a good act which can
produce not only the physical and psychological benefits that
a kind God has ordained for it, but that it is a source of
spiritual grace as well. Furthermore it is part of God's plan
whereby the human race is perpetuated, man is in some
way continued in his children, families are born, and new
souls are brought forth to return to God.

The marital act is designed to bring about the union of
the sperm and the egg. This is the primary purpose of the
act. The release of tension, the personal, intimate union of
the partners, and the fulfillment of personal desire are God-
given blessings in marriage and are almost as important as
the primary end of the act, but are the obviously necessary
human elements. These human elements are of great importance to the individual couple in their ability to affect the
sensation that they have become one, but the real way in
which they complete each other is in the union of the sperm
and the egg. The fact that the sperm and the egg do not
always join is of no particular importance except in periodic
continence and in pregnancy. If some positive, direct means
is employed to deliberately block the union of the sperm and
the egg, then God's plan to make the couple mutually complete in the procreative process is frustrated. The generative
or creative character of the marital act has been lost. The

immorality of contraception is not so much that it may prevent a possible pregnancy, but that it interferes with the natural process of the reproductive act, a function which has been entrusted to the partners by God, which trust the partners are now violating. As Pius XI stated, "Since, therefore, the conjugal act is destined primarily by nature for the begetting of children, those who in exercising it deliberately frustrate its natural power and purpose, sin against nature and commit a deed which is shameful and intrinsically evil."

The use of periodic continence, whether on the basis of a calculated safe period or thermal temperature charts, is something else again. It is abstinence; it is *not* doing something, and not to do something is morally neutral depending upon the validity of the reasons for the abstinence. To abstain from the marital act in certain periods of the month involves an element of self-discipline and self-sacrifice on the part of the members of the partnership. If this is a self-abnegation and a self-denial which is for the good of the partnership and for the good of the family—in other words, it has some valid justification—then the use of periodic continence is good. In his allocution to the midwives, Pius XII mentioned that there were four indications for the use of periodic continence, and he named them as medical, eugenic, economic, and social.

Medical Reasons for the Use of Periodic Continence

1. Recent pregnancy. Even for the woman who desires a large family, it is reasonable to assume that she might like to have several months to a year elapse between her children.
2. If pregnancy offers unusual difficulties, for example, the

patient is afflicted with arthritis, multiple sclerosis, or some limiting disease.

3. Pregnancy offers an unusual physical burden, for example, a cardiac for whom pregnancy, or repeated pregnancies, would not be wise though possible, and for whom pregnancy might entail months of bedrest.

4. Defective, retarded children, or children requiring special, extra, or prolonged care, for example, children with cerebral palsy, paralytic polio, or congenital hips, while under therapy.

5. Severe cardiac disease in the husband. In such instances the actual effort of the marital act might be a threat to his life or health. In any case, his life expectancy due to his cardiac status might be guarded enough to make it almost certain that future children would grow to adult life without a father.

6. Malignant disease in either parent.

7. Significant mental illness (not necessarily psychosis) in either parent. Some people are simply unable to assume responsibility and any additional burden such as a baby, a car, or a house might trigger a relapse.

8. It should be noted that if the life of either partner is jeopardized by the performance of the act or by pregnancy—the only real solution is the one solution which one would logically expect from two people genuinely in love —total abstinence. (What can I do *for* You?)

Eugenic Reasons for the Use of Periodic Continence

There are doubtless many instances when rhythm is legitimate on a eugenic basis. However, eugenic reasons are either reasonably common, very rare, or very dramatic, so we have selected one of each variety to give as examples.

1. Rh incompatibility. Actually, this disease should be called by its proper name, erythroblastosis fetalis; this disease can be caused not only by the Rh, but also by the incompatibilities involving blood types A, B, and O. However, the most common ones involve the Rh factor of the blood, and the ones involving A, B, and O are generally of much milder significance. Possibly 85 per cent of the population is Rh positive and 15 per cent are Rh negative. Some who are Rh positive are heterozygous. This means that they can procreate children who are either positive or negative. As a result, something between 5 and 7 per cent of all Rh negative women married to Rh positive men have babies involved with erythroblastosis fetalis. This is a disease in which the baby develops jaundice and anemia. The jaundice and anemia result because the positive factor in the baby's blood has broken through the afterbirth and mixed with the mother's blood, in which is then developed an anti-positive factor which is sent back to the baby's blood stream, where it attacks the baby's blood, destroys it, and produces anemia and jaundice. This does not happen in every situation in which an Rh negative woman is married to an Rh positive man for reasons that are not entirely clear. Sensitization can occur in any baby, that is, first or otherwise, but usually not before the third or fourth child. If the husband is heterozygous, that is he can procreate either positive or negative babies, then obviously the Rh negative babies born of such a union will not be involved. The treatment of the disease is its recognition in the unborn child as soon as possible, the delivery of the child while

still viable followed by the use of transfusions, replacement, or otherwise to correct the baby's anemia and jaundice.

If the wife is Rh negative and the husband is Rh positive, they are homozygous (i.e., all of the babies will be Rh positive), and on the third or fourth pregnancy if a baby is seriously involved, it is probable that all subsequent babies will be involved, and, therefore, there is a very good reason for the use of periodic continence.

2. Huntington's Chorea. This is a rare neurological disease which generally strikes people between the ages of thirty and forty-five, and it is a progressive and deteriorating disease. It is rare, except in certain families. It is an hereditary disease, and either parent may transmit the disease to the child. No treatment is yet known. Obviously in a marriage where this incurable disease is found in the family of either partner there is adequate eugenic reason for the use of periodic continence.

3. Pancreatic fibrosis or fibrocystic disease of the pancreas or mucoviscidosis. This is a disease which is very dramatic, has only been known for the past twenty years, and about which very little is as yet known. It is estimated that it occurs in one to one thousand, to one to ten thousand of the population. The disease is generally diagnosed in small infants. These babies are very susceptible to pulmonary infection, fail to gain weight, and are quite susceptible to heat prostration. Since this is also a disease that has a hereditary linkage, no family is required to have a large family or even successive children who will probably be involved with a disease which requires a great deal of care, whose prognosis is not yet known, and which is still under a great deal of investigation.

Economic Reasons for the Use of Periodic Continence

1. Unemployment—temporary, long-term, or chronic—in blighted areas.
2. Work injuries. Most of these are cared for in some degree by workmen's compensation or insurance, but there are still instances in which this compensation is woefully inadequate for the size of the family.
3. Serious illness. Whenever doctors talk about serious illness in this regard they are always reminded of a condition known as a rupture of a diverticulum of the bowel. This is the rupture of a little sac that has formed in the wall of the bowel. The bursting of the sac causes abscess and peritonitis. This is known as the most expensive long-term, benign disease in medicine. If this strikes the breadwinner, he can generally be assured of being out of work and semi-invalided between nine months and one year.
4. Unusual family responsibilities, for example, care of the aged in the family.
5. Constant economic failure due to:
   (A) lack of money sense in either partner.
   (B) lack of proper vocational guidance or training. In such a situation we find a rather tragic individual who is much too bright for the job which he is now doing but has not had sufficient training to justify a promotion or an advancement.
   (C) The problem of the unskilled laborer which is similar to the above but on a lower level of the laboring ladder.
   (D) Major or minor catastrophes involving members of the family physically, mentally, or legally, **or**

involving property losses which produce a drain on the family resources.

(E) The cost of feeding, clothing, and educating children, though ungrudgingly met, is to anyone facing the problem, particularly under a budget, startlingly difficult.

Social Reasons for the Use of Periodic Continence

Four social categories generally are considered to justify periodic continence.

1. War is the first. Where the husband expects to be sent to a combat or danger zone and there exists the possibility that he may not return, the couple may use periodic continence because the wife might have to rear the child all by herself. It is worth commenting that during the last war many couples did not subscribe to this thinking. However, in military life, even today, the uneven nature of the life and the constant shifting of assignment and station may represent a problem that can only be adequately solved by periodic continence.

2. Education is the second. Since World War II the search for education and the desire for early marriage have produced a natural conflict that makes periodic continence on a temporary basis necessary, justified on the grounds that the couple are acting for the good of the family.

3. Housing is the third. This generally means that:

   (A) There is no adequate housing available at the moment in a community.

   (B) There is adequate housing, but at the moment it is financially impossible.

   (C) Because both of these factors are operating to

some extent the couple is living with relatives. This can, at times, be a compatible situation, but it is notoriously intolerable for any length of time and when enforced by circumstances for any period. Periodic continence here is definitely licit. A family needs quarters in which to grow and in which to feel like a family. This requires some modicum of space and privacy and freedom from even benevolent interference.

4. Unusual occupation is the fourth. Diplomatic service with varied short-term assignments, living out of suitcases, and roving assignments with industry, particularly those that are international in character, are all valid. These assignments are usually for a period of one to two years; sometimes they are a steppingstone to promotion, but in any case, they make family living difficult, and the home life temporarily, at least, receives less attention while duty and its social obligations are apparently better served.

It should be pointed out that the struggling young American with a mortgaged home, second-hand car, working one-and-a-half jobs, with two or three children, and with no immediate prospects for a promotion, may find that several of the above indications fit his situation. The couple then can agree to use periodic continence if a fair judging of their situation seems to indicate justification, and if they can do it. Should there be doubt in their minds, they should consult a priest or a responsible counselor.

The Nature of Periodic Continence

Periodic continence is generally referred to under the general category of rhythm. This intriguing word, rhythm, refers to the fact that there is a natural cycle or rhythm to every woman's menstrual life. In other words, a woman tends to have her periods more or less regularly at approximately monthly intervals. Within this menstrual cycle, however, there is also an ovulation cycle, or an ovulation rhythm. In other words, within any given menstrual cycle, or month, there is a time which occurs with more or less regularity in which the woman will produce an egg and, therefore, can become pregnant. There is a third rhythm operating here. This rhythm involves temperature. A woman's temperature taken at basal conditions, that is, before getting out of bed in the morning, will be more or less constant and more or less low until that time of the month when she produces her egg; then it generally shifts to a higher level in response to the hormone progesterone that is liberated in her body after ovulation. Thus the temperature from month to month indicates, in rhythmic fashion, that she has or has not ovulated.

The original rhythm was pointed out by Doctors Kyusaku Ogino of Japan and Hermann Knaus of Austria. These two gentlemen, working independently, about thirty years ago pointed out that most women have a certain degree of regularity in their menstrual cycles. They also pointed out that there was a reasonable relationship between the time in which a woman produced her egg and her next expected period. It might be well to emphasize here that there is relatively little relationship found between the current period and her next ovulation. The relationship which has been established for many years now is between the production of the egg (ovulation) and *the period which the woman has not had yet*.

The principles involved seem to be relatively simple, and one is tempted to inquire why so many people have so many misgivings about the use of rhythm; there certainly is much disenchantment about rhythm, to say nothing of confusion.

When Ogino and Knaus first published their findings and recommendations, the general reaction of the medical profession was one of healthy skepticism. It must be remembered that it was not too many years ago when, "according to the best medical advice," women were being advised to avoid pregnancy by having intercourse at that time of the month which we now know to be the only time that women can conceive. So the work of Ogino and Knaus actually amounted to a complete reversal of the "best medical information." Physicians react clinically, as they must, rather slowly to new ideas. It isn't that they are reluctant to use new ideas, but they view them with grave concern. Naturally, this is for the protection of the patient. There are two dicta in medicine which are applicable here. The first is that it takes ten years to find out what any new concept, procedure, or new drug will do *to and for* the patient. The second is that everything in medicine must be proven all over again every twenty years.

Another reason why there is so much confusion about rhythm is a very human one. Just as it is well known in the legal profession that people commonly do not read the fine print in the contract, so in medicine, patients avidly reach for a new drug and forget the ground rules or instructions that go with it. In the matter of family limitation, people naturally, being human beings, want something magic pulled out of a hat, and they don't realize that *much information must be obtained about the woman, her cycle, and its variations before rhythm can be used intelligently.*

When rhythm was first formulated, physicians and social workers immediately divided as they always do, into pro and con. It soon became obvious that those who knew actually little or nothing about rhythm were captivated by its theory. Others who studied rhythm found it could work, but it required much information from the woman and interest, intelligence, and self-discipline on the part of the couple. Even then, as we will see, there remains a small percentage for whom it just will not work.

As indicated before, the basis for the rhythm cycle is the menstrual cycle. It has been stated that the average girl (who's found in textbooks) has thirteen periods a year, or approximately one every twenty-eight days. One study which involved a thousand women conscientiously keeping a record of their periods for a calendar year elicited *one* woman who had her period every twenty-eight days during that period of time. When taking a menstrual history from women, doctors commonly ask, "How often are your periods?" The answer eight times out of ten is "every twenty-eight days," until a record is asked for or until further questioning produces details which indicate that the cycle varies anywhere from twenty-five to thirty-two days. As a matter of fact, within medical circles, twenty-eight days plus or minus four is considered a normal variation for the average woman.

At the same time (*varium et mutabile semper femina*), every doctor occasionally sees a woman who has her cycle pretty regularly every twenty-two to twenty-four days or every thirty-five to thirty-seven days. This simply means that these are their normal variations and that such cycles are normal for them. The menstrual cycle, therefore, in most women can be *roughly predicted if a record of the menstrual cycle is available for a sufficiently long period of time.* For example, one complete year's record of the menstrual cycle is generally sufficient to predict that particular woman's menstrual cycle. If, in the course of a single calendar year, the woman shows no more variation than every twenty-eight to thirty days (the most common variation), then it probably will remain as such. We can feel reasonably certain of this because in the course of a single calendar year the average woman will, sometime or other, run through the common gamut of emotional and physical factors which affect her menstrual cycle.

Generally, fourteen days after ovulation a woman can expect her next menstrual period, if pregnancy does not take place. This is a reasonably constant figure based upon a fairly broad and generous experience of some forty years. It is only fair warning, however, to state that most doctors say that "usually" and "probably" about two weeks or fourteen days after ovulation, or about as close to that as you could normally expect a woman to be, she will have her next period.

Occasionally a woman ovulates early in the month; as a matter of fact, many doctors believe that for those patients who follow a rhythm cycle faithfully for a year or two and then unexplainably get pregnant, it is because the woman suddenly has ovulated early. If a woman is going to ovulate at an unusual time she will usually ovulate earlier rather than later in the month. Some women very, very occasionally ovulate during the menstrual period and others as early as the eighth menstrual cycle day; however, ovulation usually occurs on the fifteenth day before the menstruation—or to put it another way, the next period follows fourteen days after ovulation (some authorities say fourteen to sixteen days before the next expected period). The obvious value of knowing this date, even within limits, is in the knowledge that the average egg lives in a state capable of fertilization for probably not more than twenty hours. The sperm, although it may live for considerably longer periods, is capable of fertilizing an egg for probably not more than twenty-four to forty-eight hours. (These limits are subject to some variation.) The obvious problem of rhythm, therefore, is to set up a formula for an individual couple which will calculate the possible days of ovulation and take into consideration the life cycles of the egg and the sperm.

Thus, if we take a woman whose cycle is twenty-eight to thirty days and subtract fourteen days, we see that she can ovulate, theoretically at least, between her fourteenth and sixteenth day. If, however, the sperm is capable of fertilizing for forty-eight hours after it is deposited in the vagina in the marriage act, then theoretically and practically, at least two safety days prior to the time of ovulation should be interpolated here. Thus, fourteen minus two leaves the twelfth day. Since the egg conceivably can live for approximately twenty hours after ovulation, we add one day to day sixteen and we have the seventeenth day. Thus, such a woman would have a *theoretical* fertile period from the twelfth to the seventeenth day. Experience, however, has made us cautious, and most doctors recommend abstinence for six days before the earliest time of ovulation and for four days after the latest time of ovulation. Thus, in such a woman, the general advice would be to abstain from the eighth day of the cycle (day one of the period equals the first day of the cycle) to the twenty-first day of the cycle.

Problems in Periodic Continence

The real problems which are associated with rhythm and making it work successfully are as follows:

1. A very accurate record of a girl's menstrual cycles for a year is vitally important—and difficult to get. It is surprising how many women, especially women who are interested in rhythm, forget to keep a record of this important function. This record, by the way, is much more important than slide rules and other gadgets which unwittingly give a wrong impression by making things "too easy."

2. Menstruation may be affected by a number of things. The regularity of the flow is subject to variation depending upon (a) psychological disturbances, for example, grief, a striking emotional experience of any kind, sudden catastrophe, or sudden, amazing good luck within the family; (b) Physical problems such as serious illness, high fever, surgery of the female or other organs, change in occupation, or change in the type of living—for example a girl going away to a boarding school or college. A change of climate and injury to the abdomen involving the area of the pelvic organs may also affect menstruation; (c) Hormonal disturbances of a varying and usually rather mysterious nature; (d) Following pregnancy a girl may establish the same cycle or may establish a new cycle, and sometimes it takes several months before this can be worked out and proven together with its variations.

3. Some women have menstrual cycles which are completely irregular, for example, every twenty to thirty-five to sixty-one days. Such women, with no known pattern to their menstrual cycles, cannot profit from the usual rhythm advice. Any woman whose menstrual cycles vary greater than ten days between given months is generally not amenable to proper rhythm advice. Her only alternatives are the temperature method or total abstinence.

4. Rhythm in the first year of married life may not be very efficient. Although this statement comes as something of a shock to some people and is unwelcome to many others, the plain facts of the matter are that in the first year of married life, rhythm (or any method of birth regulation for that matter) is not apt to be a very practical measure. The accuracy of the cycles and the ex-

perience with the menstrual cycles is not yet well-established in most cases. A year's record of the menstrual cycle is notoriously absent. Unless the motivation is unusual, the average girl does not have a sufficient knowledge of her cycle or its accuracy to allow the doctor to give the proper information. Rhythm in the first year of married life means making love by a calendar, and young people in love find it extremely difficult to tear away from the natural spontaneity of the act to involve themselves with rhythm.

It should be pointed out, however, that all is not lost; rhythm *can* be made to work in the first year of married life. It simply requires considerable motivation and may involve an heroic effort on the part of the couple. Most physicians and marriage counselors who see a couple in their first year of married life making rhythm work, generally attribute their success to the love they have for one another and their willingness to give up this much for a common good. However, it should be pointed out in all fairness that it might be well for a couple embarking on marriage to prove first of all that they can have a child before they make such heroic efforts to insure that they don't. When the partners are over twenty-five particularly, the presumption is that any couple able to make rhythm work successfully in the first year of married life may be avoiding pregnancy because of a basic infertility rather than the successful rhythm.

5. The most common medical entity obstetricians see is pregnancy, and the next most common is the inability to become pregnant.

6. One of the great American "sins of presumption" is that in this great, healthy country of ours everyone is as fertile as the rabbit in the field. The truth of the matter is

that one in six marriages have an infertility problem, and that one in five to eight pregnancies ends up as a miscarriage.

If rhythm, therefore, is difficult for some people or impossible for others, what form of periodic continence do we have available for them? The basic problem remains the same. How can we determine and pinpoint with greater accuracy the time of ovulation? There are numerous tests for ovulation. Some are better than others, and some are impractical for home use. Two common clinical signs of ovulation which can be detected with some accuracy in probably forty per cent of women are:

1. Pain, one side or the other, low down in the abdomen at the time of ovulation. This is known as Mittelschmerz, or middle pain, indicating the rupture of the egg from the ovary.
2. The discharge from the vagina of a colorless, glary mucus which may be tinged with blood, again occurring near mid-cycle at the time of ovulation.

In some few women, these signs are highly accurate; in others reasonably accurate. For large groups of people, however, these tests seemingly have no value. The difficulty lies in the fact that *ovulation may occur before or after the pain.* Therefore, most people have to turn to what is generally referred to as the basal temperature chart.

The Basal Temperature Chart

The basal temperature is the temperature at resting conditions, sometimes called the lowest normal temperature reading in a given day. From broad experience, we know this occurs after a night's sleep while a woman is still in bed, before she has had anything to eat, drink, or smoke. (The afternoon temperature is apt to be normally somewhat higher.) Under these basal conditions, if a thermometer is left in a woman's mouth for *five* minutes and the temperature accurately charted, her temperature, in general, will remain somewhere between 97° F. and 98° F. Once a woman ovulates, her temperature rises between .1° F. and .8° F. Following ovulation, this elevation in temperature remains until shortly before the period, when it returns to the previous low, normal level. The rise in temperature is caused by the release in the body of a female hormone (the hormone of the mother) called progesterone. This *normally* occurs immediately after ovulation. *Occasionally,* however, the release of the progesterone may precede or follow ovulation by forty-eight hours and thus, the temperature chart may show an apparent error of forty-eight hours in either direction in pinpointing ovulation. This is why the charts should be followed monthly by a physician and periodically evaluated at other times. Some charts, for example, the "staircase chart," can be difficult to read and may require careful interpretation by a physician.

This, then, is the origin of the so-called biphasic curve of temperature. From the beginning of the menstrual flow until ovulation, the temperature may fluctuate slightly but will remain within a relatively low level. Following ovulation, the temperature rises anywhere from .1° to .8° F.; it then has entered a new phase. The point at which the temperatures switch from one phase to the other is generally considered to be the time of ovulation. In some women, occasionally there will be a drop in temperature just at the point of this change or, as it is sometimes put, a sudden drop followed by a rise. This is not established as uniform for all women, nor is it found commonly in a great many women.

Obviously, accurate measuring of the temperature and accurate charting of the temperature are important. Our own best experience has been to have the wife take the temperature, and the husband to keep the chart. With both of them involved, and both understanding what is meant by a biphasic curve or by the thermal shift from one level of temperature to another, results have been quite satisfactory in the vast majority of patients. The accompanying illustration demonstrates one, a typical chart; two, a biphasic curve; and three, a biphasic curve superimposed on a typical chart.

There are two things to be sought in a temperature chart. The first is to be able to recognize the biphasic curve month after month. The second is to recognize the pattern of the ovulation-menstruation cycle. Thus, some couples, after a year of charting, find that the girl never ovulates before the tenth day. Since the difficulty with the chart is that it only informs you that ovulation has already taken place, if the couple knows that the girl never ovulates before the tenth day, then they may have relations certainly up to the seventh day with safety, and they may resume relations three days after the thermal shift with the biphasic curve in evidence. The temperature chart allows some patients to cut the period of abstinence from two weeks (under rhythm) to one week.

Among the methods of determining ovulation which have been developed recently is a very intriguing one originally described by Dr. Charles Birnberg of Brooklyn, New York.* Dr. Birnberg used a reducing tape, a piece of paper impregnated with a chemical which would react by changing color in the presence of a simple sugar or glucose. It had been determined some time before that glucose or a similar substance was present in the neck of the womb (or the cervix) of the woman at the time of ovulation. Using a very simple

---

* J.A.M.A., March 8, 1958. 166:1174.

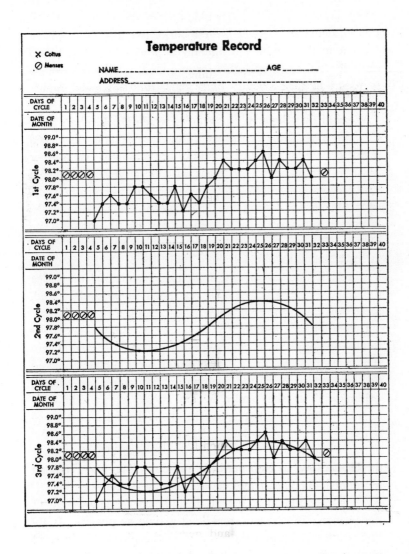

tape, and using it under ideal conditions, that is, in the office every day, Dr. Birnberg was able to pinpoint successfully the time of ovulation in twenty-three out of twenty-seven women. Such a method, while intriguing, is obviously not practical since it would be impossible for any great number of women to report to their doctor's office daily for such a determination.

We said that the conditions under which Dr. Birnberg used the tape were ideal. By this we mean that the tape was placed in the cervix without any danger of contamination from other sources. There are other areas in and around the vagina which contain a reacting substance more or less all the time, so if the patient herself uses the tape in her own body she is apt to get a positive test every day of the month. The Fertility Testor has been developed by Doyle and Ewers in an attempt to obviate these difficulties. At the moment, however, it remains merely a promising and intriguing idea the accuracy of which still leaves much to be desired and, therefore, cannot be recommended except on a research basis.

Limitation of the family is obviously a family function. It should not—indeed, it *cannot*—be a unilateral decision. There should be good reasons for such limitation; the couple should feel comfortable with the decision and periodically review it.

Limitation of the family by any means of periodic continence is not easy, but it can be done. Periodic continence requires strong motivation and mutual respect between the partners and for the family and the common life; it requires the cooperation of both partners, self-discipline, and Christian self-denial—for Christ and for the family. It requires knowledge of the principles behind it and specific knowledge of the woman's function over as long a time as possible. It requires interest by and direction from the physician. In most instances it will work, but it must be *made* to work.

In rare instances the only solution is total or almost total abstinence. These are grave situations and require an heroic effort for the welfare of at least one of the parents or the family. It is uncomfortable, it is difficult, it is even at times almost tragic—but it is neither abnormal nor impossible, and abstinence may well be what the partners must do *for* one another.

10

Pregnancy and the New Baby

Pregnancy is the most wonderful story in nature. In the light of modern attitudes on pregnancy this easily is forgotten. So much of modern writing treats pregnancy only as a biological process. At times, it is looked upon even as a social nuisance because it is the means by which population increases. Wherever pregnancy flourishes, therefore, it is most attacked. We hear and read much about the control of pregnancy, the regulation of pregnancy, the necessity of making pregnancy safer, and the necessity of producing pregnancies which will represent a better and higher type of human than we have had heretofore. But in all this discussion, we forget to keep in perspective what pregnancy really is.

Pregnancy is the beginning of a family. It is the loan of a soul to two people in love who, with their love, may nourish the soul and send it back to God. Pregnancy is the process by which the wife becomes a mother and the husband becomes a father; the process by which the wife brings into the world the fruit of the love that they have nourished together. Pregnancy is a personal business filled with happiness, joy, pride, work, and plans. Pregnancy is the supreme human accomplishment and far surpasses any other work of man in mystery, efficiency, and happiness; it is the right of all men of any and all stations in life, a right which must be used with wisdom and reason, bearing in mind true compassion for all members of the family. Pregnancy is one of the basic common denominators of people.

There is much that is sentimental about pregnancy but the entire story is real. It represents the future of the world, the means by which man himself may be perpetuated through the ages. Pregnancy offers a woman her greatest experience and offers a man a real sense of fulfillment as he watches his child grow tall, become a better person than he, and make a greater contribution to this world.

Symptoms of Pregnancy

How is pregnancy diagnosed? There are certain symptoms and signs. Perhaps the most common symptom of pregnancy is fatigue from doing nothing and the most constant sign the absence of menstrual periods in a person who previously has been regular. Nausea and vomiting are not at all the most common symptoms of pregnancy. Something less than 40 per cent of women have them. Some women have nausea and vomiting only if there is associated fatigue from lack of rest, for example, a woman who has several other small children. Many women have no vomiting at all and very little nausea. The fascinating thing about these women is that since they do not have nausea and vomiting, they are not news (after all one doesn't announce that one has not broken one's leg today), and because they are not news, no one talks about them. Thus the girl who is unhappy and ill is the one who sets the pattern. She "makes news" with her relatives and friends and other women in the neighborhood, and the resultant impression is that the girl who isn't having much nausea and vomiting "simply couldn't be pregnant."

The pregnancy symptom that annoys a woman most, and irritates her husband because he does not understand it, is fatigue from doing nothing. This seems to be a sort of natural safety valve which nature places in the pregnant woman, especially in the early months, as a means of deterring her from painting the town red while she carries on her normal living. This fatigue comes rather suddenly and, of course, is most noted in the vivacious girl who has always been famous for her willingness to "drop everything and run."

Because of this fatigue, a pregnant woman may have little or no desire for the act of love, although most women will have resurgent episodes in which their desire for loving is intense. One of the most common questions of engaged and married couples concerns the problem of the marital act during pregnancy. No one can give an adequate, specific answer to this in a general discussion of the problem for obvious reasons. Not only is the love-act a particular and personal matter, but so is pregnancy. Most husbands, aided and abetted by their wives in this respect, gradually learn to understand the situation and act accordingly. The only outside person who can give adequate advice on this subject is the physician who is taking care of a woman during her pregnancy.

As for the dangers involved in intercourse during pregnancy, it is almost certainly established today that no normally implanted pregnancy can be disturbed without almost deliberate intervention. It is equally well-established that in the vast majority of cases of miscarriages, *the pregnancy is already dead days to weeks before the patient originally starts to bleed as the first sign of the miscarriage.* There is no serious reason to believe that in a normally implanted pregnancy there is any great danger of miscarriage at the time when the woman would normally expect her period or as the result of intercourse.

There are no magic time intervals such as a week, month, six weeks, or three months in the beginning, middle, or end of pregnancy in which it is dangerous to the woman or to the pregnancy to have marital relations. In the latter half of pregnancy most couples have to change the position in which they normally have marital relations so the husband's weight does not seriously interfere with the wife's comfort or her ability to enjoy the act. Such change of position is generally given on the advice of an individual physician. Obviously, if the woman is having any bleeding late in pregnancy, or any infection or discharge, then the couple should not, as a matter of common sense, have intercourse, but neither should she take a five-mile hike or fight the Monday morning crowd in a nearby bargain basement. Under these or any conditions, such as toxemia or elevated blood pressure, which may possibly involve some serious problem in pregnancy, the woman should seek the advice of her physician and follow it closely.

Pregnancy is the fruit of the act of love between two people. It is reasonable to expect, then, that a couple will be drawn so close together that the act might be mutually desired often during the course of the pregnancy. The general advice is that all other things being equal, and if the pregnancy is proceeding normally, a woman may while she is pregnant do anything she is accustomed to doing when she is not pregnant. Of course, only general comments can be made here. Specific advice and recommendations depend upon specific circumstances. But it should be remembered that pregnancy should be a healthy and a happy time, and in pregnancy the advice to keep things simple and let the good things happen is more pertinent than in any other area of medicine.

Changes in the breasts are fairly common in early pregnancy. The breasts become larger and heavier and, for most women, quite sore and sensitive, especially in the first six to eight weeks of pregnancy. The breasts should be properly supported, and in many cases it is worth the expense of having a support made to order. The nipples become darker, and, even at this early date, a small amount of white fluid may normally be pressed or drained from the breasts. Perhaps the most marked changes in the breasts occur in a girl who prior to pregnancy has considered herself "flat-chested." It is she who, in the familiar language of pregnancy, blossoms forth; indeed, she is usually the most successful in breast feeding.

The hair eventually becomes somewhat brittle, dry, and more difficult to manage, and the skin sometimes undergoes profound changes. In addition to darkening of the nipples, a black pigmented line may appear down the midline of the abdomen. This is the linea nigra of pregnancy. The development of numerous small pigmented moles, or pigmented spots, many of which are temporary, is not unusual in pregnancy. Similarly, soft, fleshy, or wart-like, non-pigmented growths, particularly about the face and neck, are common—and are distressing. But the vast majority of these seem to disappear quickly at the end of pregnancy. Probably the most noteworthy change in the skin is what is referred to as chloasma or the mask of pregnancy. This is a butterfly-shaped pigmented area spreading across the cheeks and the bridge of the nose. Many women carry this with pride, others with annoyance. In any case, it is rather easily controlled by cosmetics if the girl so desires.

It is literally amazing how quickly varicose veins may crop

up and produce symptoms on the legs of pregnant women. One of the first things a woman who is having her second or third baby may notice is the sudden appearance of varicose veins. The chief symptom associated with these, of course, is fatigue and what women refer to as tired legs or heavy legs of pregnancy. Various methods, from supportive stockings to injections of the veins, are available for relief at the suggestion of the physician.

Certain changes occur in the woman's internal organs (e.g., the neck of the womb becomes soft and the internal organs turn blue), but these have interest chiefly to the physician. In any case none of the above symptoms are characteristic of pregnancy alone. If in addition to these symptoms there is a history of a missed menstrual period, we have, even then, only a strong indication of pregnancy. We can say that any girl whose periods have been quite regular previously and is seven days late is automatically suspected of being pregnant until proven otherwise. But none of these indications, we repeat, are conclusive. If a woman, therefore, wishes to know as early as possible whether or not she is pregnant, other tests will have to be employed.

Tests for Pregnancy

The absolute signs of pregnancy are X-ray evidence of the bones of the baby and detection of the fetal heart tones or movements. X rays will not show a pregnancy until approximately the twentieth week and detection of the fetal heart sounds by conventional methods in the doctor's office will rarely be possible sooner than that. As the fetal electrocardiograph becomes more commonly used, we expect that in the next ten years a diagnosis of pregnancy which is definite, specific, and based upon the fetal heart tones may be possible as early as the third month. Today, however, much reliability is placed upon the "pregnancy test."

This test, which is referred to as the AZ (from Aschheim-Zondek, the two men who devised the test), commonly employs the patient's urine but may also be done using the spinal fluid or the serum portion of the blood. The pregnancy test depends upon the presence of living tissue in the afterbirth and the hormone which that tissue produces. It does not of itself give us any information as to whether the fetus is alive or dead. As a matter of fact, the pregnancy test is not specific even for pregnancy itself, since it causes a similar reaction in any tissue which is identical with the afterbirth. Such tissue is sometimes found in bizarre tumors in the testicle of the male and, of course, in tumors of the after birth in the female.

The test makes use of laboratory animals such as rabbits, mice, rats, frogs, and toads. It usually takes about five hours to get complete results. The earliest date that a test can be positive is usually the thirty-ninth menstrual day. After the fiftieth day it is better than 95 per cent accurate. Laboratory error may give false positive or false negative tests early in the pregnancy, but none of these is commonly encountered in a good laboratory. Very rarely is there a patient who is obviously pregnant and in whom the pregnancy test is repeatedly negative until about the fifth month.

The basal body temperature, charted as described in the chapter "Limitation of the Family," is also a reliable test of pregnancy. Should the temperature remain up at post ovulatory levels for forty days or more, we have then what is called the poor man's Aschheim-Zondek test, and it is considered by most authorities to be positive for pregnancy.

For many years science has been seeking a chemical or an immunological test for pregnancy. These have involved either a simple chemical test on the urine or blood in the laboratory or a skin test of the mother. In the past their reliability has left something to be desired. More recently such laboratory tests requiring only five to thirty minutes to perform have been materially improved to the point where it seems that the near future will offer us a reliable, rapid, and simple test of pregnancy.

Behavior During Pregnancy

Once the diagnosis of pregnancy has been established, a minor revolution takes place in the lives of the couple concerned, particularly if it is the first time. Many a pregnancy suddenly has turned the happy-go-lucky, day-dreaming husband into the "plans-and-training officer" for the family. His new sense of responsibility often is frightening to him, but the pregnancy rapidly becomes the challenge of his life. Sometimes for the first time a young husband suddenly ceases to think at all of himself and becomes a protective creature vitally concerned with his wife and child. He becomes Kipling's "Reservest of the line"—a man who must either sink or swim—"and he can't afford to sink." He looks at his wife from a new point of view; no longer concerned merely with love and pride, he now develops a concept of safety and what it means and entails. He acquires a new possessiveness, a new sense of oneness with the woman he loves. Now, indeed, they are accomplishing something together.

In army parlance, he takes a new estimate of his own situation. He critically evaluates his job, his future, and his security. If his calculations fail to produce an ideal answer, he may become agitated or confused. Very occasionally physicians see men under these circumstances go into acute reactive depressions, a sort of "pre-baby blues," as problems of pride, responsibility, security, and safety are suddenly thrust upon someone who is a perfectionist and who somehow feels inadequate and insecure. One of the main difficulties is that in his masculine role a man is not supposed to demonstrate his worry or show his concern; he is supposed to be always calm and self-assured—but not infrequently his self-confidence is on the line or he is running scared.

Unfortunately, communication on this very important subject of pregnancy and the man's reaction to it is difficult, at times even impossible. So it is not surprising if a girl complains that her husband does not seem to be particularly aware of her problems. There are really three reasons for this: The first is the lack of communication between the two people. Any lack of communication hurts. The second is the man's preoccupation with his own problems or what he thinks they are. The third is that the husband knows so little about pregnancy and its effect upon women.

Pregnancy for a woman is more than a biological process, more than mere feelings of joy and happiness. Since she was born for it, she finds in pregnancy her greatest fulfillment as a woman. It is an unusual woman who does not appreciate her unique role in cooperating with the person she loves most and with her Creator to bring the flesh of her flesh into the world as a living, vibrant, and loving thing.

The average girl enters pregnancy apprehensively. It is a new experience for her and one of the biggest, if not *the* biggest thing that happens to her. Some women are not particularly aware of the pregnancy itself until the baby begins to move, which is usually some time during the fifth month. At this point, she may be somewhat confused and apprehensive until she suddenly realizes, or has it pointed out to her (sometimes by the obstetrician), that she now has someone who is totally dependent upon her. From that point on she has a daily reminder that it is her function in life to carry love.

The pregnant woman's biggest responsibility is to seek and practice adequate prenatal care. A mother's primary function is to nourish her baby—indeed, in pregnancy it is the only thing that she can do for it. The sex of the baby is already determined. The size of the baby will depend upon the inherited genes; the color of the hair and eyes are all determined and beyond the mother's control. The one thing that she can offer to her child is nourishment. She has nine months in which to prepare herself and her baby for any possible surgical emergency that might arise, to prepare herself and her baby as much as possible against infection, and to simplify the sometimes arduous task of delivery. Much of prenatal care is concerned with proper diet. The mother's diet is calculated to offer growth, resistance to infection, and stamina to herself and to her baby. The physician will check her weight, blood pressure, urine, and whatever else is required to determine if the pregnancy is proceeding normally and to gather the necessary information to offer further advice for the ensuing month. A proper and strict diet stresses weight control, since there is little, if anything, that can be said in favor of excess weight gained in pregnancy.

The emphasis in prenatal care should always be on the importance of having a happy and healthy pregnancy. Sometimes the biggest hazard to any girl's successful pregnancy is the attention of well-intentioned other women. Old-wives' tales, interference with the physician's advice, lists of prohibitions as inane as they are long, advice which is solemnly given and thoroughly inaccurate—these are the things which confuse and worry a woman and from which she needs protection by her husband. Pregnancy is safest and easiest when a woman follows her physician's advice.

The New Baby

The new baby should be the object of love and affection just as it is the symbol of a family. It is most discouraging to hear discussions about the selfishness of the mother in keeping the baby from the father or to read an erudite article on the jealousy patterns of the father. A baby is small, but it is capable of receiving all the love which both mother and father can offer it. Similarly, it has an inexhaustible supply available for both parents. When a new baby is brought into the home, it should be the primary responsibility and interest of the parents. A baby should not be too precious, too brittle, or too fragile for the father to hold or to help care for. Babies are meant to be shared with grandparents and other select members of the family; they are a source of family pride. But by the same token they are not museum pieces to be constantly picked up, fondled, and breathed upon by every interested relative, neighbor, and friend, however well-intentioned.

Many of the difficulties associated with the new baby in the home arise from the fact that a new baby is almost irresistible to anyone with a basic human instinct. Everyone wants to get into the act, and from everyone comes an unceasing stream of advice. Perhaps nowhere else in medicine is the ancient Japanese expression "Too many sailors make the ship go up the mountain" more appropriate. Someone who has brought up three to twelve children does not necessarily know anything about bringing up a particular baby. Decisions with regard to a baby's food, clothing, and living quarters should be the primary responsibility of even the neophyte parents, aided by the physician's advice. Every parent has the right to make mistakes. A parent's natural instinct for the supreme care of the child usually will prevent serious mistakes; it will send him or her to seek objective advice where it can be obtained—from the physician.

Whenever pregnancy and the new baby are discussed the question of breast feeding arises. Indeed, breast feeding seems to be a woman's natural and instinctive concern. In modern-day living, however, this instinctive concern is usually promptly squelched. Breast feeding has been so discouraged over the past thirty years in the United States that the average girl who wants to nurse her baby has to struggle to do so. She is told that her breasts will be bigger—and smaller—if she nurses; that breast feeding is cow-like or animal-like; that it ties the mother down; that it is time-consuming and embarrassing. These statements can generally be traced to women who have never nursed. In recent years more women have turned to nursing, so now for every three experts who have such strong opinions on the subject but who have never nursed, there is the one woman who has successfully nursed and who very efficiently and quietly manages to offset the other three. Of course, there is still with us, the most loudly declaiming expert of all, the woman who *has* nursed—for one week.

Breast feeding has no effect on the size or shape of the breasts. As a matter of fact, a girl with small breasts is generally quite disappointed to see her breasts return to their normal size after pregnancy and nursing. And I am somewhat nonplussed by the attitude of those who consider breast feeding to be animal-like or cow-like. This apparently is one of those situations where not only is the point of view decidedly different, but a deep understanding of the birth process and the instinctive maternal care of the child is missing.

In adult society breast feeding should not be embarrassing —the woman simply takes her baby to another room and feeds it. As for the effect of breast feeding on small children in the home, most women who nurse their babies in the presence of other children in the home find that the children are at first quite interested in the process but quickly become bored. Breast feeding also presents a natural and convenient situation for a child to bring up questions which lead to the proper basis for his sex education. In this respect, and on this subject, it is *less* embarrassing for both the mother and the child.

A mother who nurses her baby is not particularly tied down since it is possible to acclimate a breast-feeding baby to almost any schedule. Furthermore, most mothers with small babies are not particularly happy to be away from their baby for long periods of time. Any woman can maintain a very successful social life (e.g., going out to a show and dinner) while nursing, although it must be admitted that she can't stop for a midnight snack on the way home.

There are many positive aspects to breast feeding. It will be sufficient for our purposes to enumerate only some of its advantages—for the mother and her baby:

1. It is a special food which a kind God has given to the mother for her baby.

2. It is always available and at the right temperature.

3. It is always sterile.

4. The quantity can be regulated by the baby himself, because the vigor of the baby's nursing determines the quantity of milk which will be available at the next feeding time.

5. The babies feel cuddled and wanted while they are being fed. It might be added, too, that the mother feels wanted—and needed as well.

6. In the early days of its life, a breast-fed baby is likely to be much more alert and have quicker reflexes than the bottle-fed baby, although it must be admitted that at the end of one year, no difference can be elicited.

7. A breast-fed baby derives a natural immunity to those diseases to which the mother is also immune as a result of the antibodies (defense substances) contained in the breast milk.

8. Because the average mother who is breast feeding her child must be with the child during its feeding and because this is the time when observations of an infant are likely to be most rewarding, it is not unusual for the mother of a breast-feeding baby to know much more about her child than the mother who is artificially feeding her baby.

9. Breast-fed babies almost universally are happy, content, and tractable.

Among the primitive peoples (who are often not so primitive as poor), mothers, who have nothing else to give babies except their breast milk, may offer this for as long as nine months. They do not become pregnant, even among those tribes in which the people feel a mandate to have as many children as possible; the babies are rarely born closer than twenty months apart. Nature provides a relatively secure (and very secure when utilized properly) built-in control of the size of the family—a mechanism whereby a nursing baby, vigourously sucking at his mother's nipple, stimulates the breast to produce milk and at the same time prevents the pituitary glands from producing those hormones which are necessary for the production of an egg. A woman can nurse her baby without fear of an intervening pregnancy, but the process must be carefully regulated and the exact nature of lactation, or breast feeding, must be thoroughly understood.

By lactation we mean the process by which the mother offers to the newborn infant for a period (usually three to six months) the natural milk which she herself produces. Lactation does not refer to any other type of feeding. As a matter of fact, as properly understood, it excludes all other types of feeding, whether they be labeled "stand-by bottle," "substitution bottle," "supplementary feeding," "complementary feeding," or any other type of "feeding." As soon as a bottle is introduced into the schedule of a breast-feeding baby, the process *begins to change* from one of breast feeding to one of weaning. Regardless of the type of added feeding, or what name it is given, the fact remains that when a breast-feeding baby is weaned from its mother's breast, a bottle is substituted for one of the breast feedings. And as long as this continues, within a relatively short period of time, as I'm sure all mothers who have nursed their babies will attest, the baby is "off breast."

It must be emphasized that as a baby is coming off breast, or going through the weaning process, there is no longer the same stimulus produced by the baby at the mother's nipple to prevent ovulation. *A woman can get pregnant while she is weaning;* she does not while she is breast feeding as it is properly understood.

The question of how the introduction of solid food affects this matter is constantly brought up. In the first place, many pediatricians are opposed to feeding babies solid food, such as cereal or even fruit and fruit juices, before the sixth or the twelfth week after birth. Some pediatricians prefer to hold off giving babies these foods for even longer. Our experience has been that a small amount of solid food twice a day (the nature of it seems to be rather immaterial) after a baby has been breast-fed does not seem to interfere with the nursing process. It must be emphasized, however, that such feedings are always given after the baby is nursed and not before. On the other hand, some women who start adding solid foods at a relatively early age to their breast-feeding babies experience immediate weaning with the consequent possibility of pregnancy after intercourse.

In conclusion, each child has the right to expect that of all people on earth its mother and father will not be afraid of it. The parents may be apprehensive, and they usually are; on the whole, such apprehension is good because it is the safety valve which keeps the parents cautious. But I believe it is the experience of most doctors that a newborn infant belongs with its own mother and father in its own home. Advice and assistance are valuable—take-over practices are a menace. The parents and the child—the family—have a right to mature, and they must for the sake of society.

11

Menstruation

Most of the problems associated with menstruation have been created by the perpetuation of old wives' tales and fostered by certain fears associated with the function itself. The terminology concerning menstruation is perhaps typical of these attitudes.

It is not uncommon to hear women speak of their menstrual period as "the curse" or "the friend." Actually, menstruation is the one function which allows a woman to cooperate in the love of the person she holds dearest in the world and the love of her God to bring new life into the world. The "curse" is indicative of an attitude found in that school of thinking which considers the female of the species a poor, down-trodden, benighted, second-class type of individual.

The term "friend" originates from those women who, promiscuous in their habits, find themselves fortunate not to have become pregnant in the course of the preceding month.

To them, therefore, the appearance of the menstrual discharge is a "friend." To only a very minor degree does the term "friend" extend to the hapless woman who is married to an inconsiderate overbearing male and who already has many children who are uncared for, unwanted, or neglected.

The only healthy attitude that one can take towards security of mind in one's place in life is based upon the fundamental acceptance of what we are and what we can be. To what extent we can improve our own station and that of those whom we love is a matter of good mental hygiene and properly placed ambition. No one is presumptuous enough to say that a woman can, or necessarily should, be brought up to enjoy thoroughly the menstrual function. It has many associated symptoms that can make it rather uncomfortable. At the same time, we believe a woman should be brought up with the realization that the menstrual function actually represents her greatest privilege as a woman—that of bringing new life into the world. Giving a young teen-ager a concept of the menstrual function as the symbol of all her future ills is a sure way to develop a neurotic, self-pitying, egocentric adult who believes that because she is a woman she has been blighted by God Himself from the time of her creation.

Years ago, it was not uncommon to find a young girl coming to menstrual age totally unprepared for what might happen to her. Thanks be to God, this attitude is rapidly changing and for the better. But we still find occasionally a woman whose attitude towards herself as a woman and towards sex in general has been soured because at the age of twelve or thirteen, when the menstrual function came upon her for the first time, she was caught unaware. A girl in this situation, in the panic of finding a bloody discharge the nature of which she did not know, often turned to the first woman she met (not necessarily her mother, let it be noted) only to be told, "Don't be frightened; this is just the bad blood coming out of you." This is a particularly ugly example of the teaching to which some girls are exposed. Blood is a symbol of panic even to adults and is particularly troublesome to the young child, and the word "bad" to the average young teen-ager is still apt to be synonymous with something sinful.

Scientifically, there is nothing "bad" about the menstrual function. As already indicated, it is a perfectly normal physiological function which represents the monthly preparation for motherhood. For the "average" girl who flows from five to seven days, the amount of blood loss is generally only between one and four ounces. The menstrual flow simply represents the bed which was not used in the previous month for a pregnancy. This bed is stained by blood and is further increased in volume by the nutritive fluid which is present in the womb as a source of nourishment to a possible fertilized egg just prior to menstruation and following ovulation. It is not unusual for the average woman to pass small clots (that is, the size of one-half inch or so) in a normal menstrual flow. Occasionally, these may be represented as rather small, stringy types of clots. Clots larger than that, up to one inch in diameter, may be normal for a particular individual. Clots larger than one inch usually require some degree of investigation.

As a woman grows older, the term "menstrual function" or "menstruation" has other peculiar connotations. It is not, unhappily, uncommon to find a woman beyond her change of life who has vaginal bleeding presumably coming from her womb. It seems odd, in the light of the wide dissemination of public health information, for a woman in her early sixties to consider such bleeding as "menstruation." The concept that not all bleeding is menstruation has apparently not yet filtered down to the general public. It is one thing for a woman to skip a period occasionally. It is one thing for a woman to develop a new cycle of menstruation, for example, having her periods every twenty days where she formerly had them every twenty-eight. These disturbances of menstrual function are usually not serious and many times self-correcting; certainly, they are readily solved by a physician. But a woman who bleeds for twenty-five days at a time, or has episodes of bleeding sometimes ten days apart, sometimes forty days apart, or bleeds after the menopause, or bleeds irregularly during the menopause, does not have what properly can be called menstruation; she has true bleeding which demands investigation for possibly serious reasons.

Normal Discomforts in Menstruation

The reaction of women to menstruation varies considerably. Some women are very unhappy at menstruation, others pass the time of their period with no particular thoughts that anything unusual is happening except the nuisance of the bloody discharge. However, there are certain more or less constant symptoms which are found to some degree in all women at the time of menstruation. For example, some women develop skin blemishes, particularly on the face, just before the period. Others develop a headache or dark circles under their eyes. Still others develop some degree of irritability, depression, and/or ambition. Thirst or hunger is occasionally manifested, as is lack of appetite and dryness of the mouth. Swelling and tenderness of the breasts is a frequent accompaniment of the menstrual function in many women. Bloating of the abdomen is not only common but uncomfortable and quite disturbing to many women—there may be a gain in

weight from two to eight pounds. A heavy, dragging sensation of the pelvis is found in some women just prior to the
menstrual function. A heavy, pulling sensation in the thighs,
"heavy," "tired," or "nervous" legs are frequent at the time
of the period. Constipation and/or diarrhea, or varying degrees in either, are common. Many women have a certain
difficulty with the bowels prior to the onset of the flow
followed by some loose movements immediately after it
begins. Many women have one or more of these symptoms,
but most women ignore them and go about their usual functions. Occasionally, a woman has many of these symptoms all
at once and some of them perhaps to a very uncomfortable
degree. Such a girl is said to be involved with "premenstrual
tension."

The mechanism behind all these symptoms in an over-
simplified way is as follows: The hormones which control
pregnancy are the same hormones which control the period.
These hormones are steroids, and the steroids in the body
have an affinity for sodium. Therefore, starting usually about
ten days before the expected flow, when the steroid hormones
are at a rather high level in the woman's blood, her body
tends to retain sodium (salt, salty products, and sodium
preparations). But sodium cannot remain in the body unless
it is in solution, so at the time the body is retaining sodium
it is retaining water as well, which causes the various symptoms previously described. The perfect example is the bloating of the abdomen. Then, during the menstrual cycle, the
hormone levels drop, the steroid hormones are released, and
the water is in turn released; as a result many women have
an increased output of urine and, with an outpouring of
water into the bowel, loose movements. They feel relief and
the bloating of the abdomen disappears almost miraculously.
The simple expedient of avoiding foods containing a great
deal of salt, baking soda, or sodium preparations used as

preservatives gives considerable relief from these symptoms. Should these measures fail, physicians usually prescribe simple medications for individual cases.

The heavy, dragging sensation in the pelvis is more apt to be due to congestion of the pelvis. Congestion is a condition in which the blood fills the organs involved; thus we may say that the womb and ovaries are congested at the time of the period. The mechanism behind congestion is very simple. The menstrual cycle is the preparation every month for pregnancy, so obviously the pelvic organs, the organs of reproduction (namely, the womb, the ovaries, and the tubes), are prepared in case a pregnancy occurs. The pelvic organs must offer the nourishment to a newly-growing pregnancy, so for nourishment alone the blood supply must be prepared to encourage the growth of the early pregnancy should it occur. If, in addition, certain mechanical factors aggravate this, for example, the force of gravity, which allows blood to remain in the pelvis in a woman who is on her feet many hours of the day, then the symptoms can be conceivably worsened. School teachers, nurses, and waitresses have this occupational hazard inasmuch as they are on their feet long uninterrupted hours of the day. In addition to congestion, there may be associated menstrual cramps.

Menstrual cramps are due to contractions of the womb. They are annoying in most women and fairly severe in a few. Why these contractions should be so painful in some women and not in others, or why they should be so painful in some months and not in others, is a story which we cannot go into here because it involves theories and technical aspects of ovulation and the menstrual function and that most confusing of all subjects, women. Suffice it to say that the "normal" menstrual cramps are always in the midline, intermittent, and are colicky in character. And they are quite commonly found in the absence of any disease in the pelvic organs. There are several ways to control the discomfort associated with menstrual cramps and pelvic congestion. Nevertheless, it should be kept in mind that no one means is known to cure all people; the problem is generally a normal variant which is aggravated by the lack of proper body hygiene in some department or other; where there is a problem of general body hygiene or specific body hygiene, there is usually disinterest on the part of the patient who is looking for a more dramatic answer; and all solutions involve the use of some time and effort on the part of the patient herself.

Alleviating Normal Menstrual Discomforts

Regular exercise. The cry that American youth does not indulge in proper, regular exercise is hackneyed, but unfortunately it is quite true. Any physician who has ever treated a group of women of high school or college age will attest to the dramatic lack of menstrual difficulties to be found in the girls who are involved with basketball, field hockey, or swimming.

Proper bowel hygiene. This, of course, is also intimately associated with the diet. It has been said that no one *feels right* in the course of the day if the bowel function has been in some way suppressed. It also has been said that the average woman can always think of a thousand other things more important to do than to maintain a proper evacuation. So the average male goes through life trying to keep on good terms with his gastro-intestinal tract, and the woman constantly grapples with the problem of her bowels. Constipation at or about the time of menstruation is apt to be something more of a problem because of fluid retention; but constipation is also one of the factors in the development of congestion, therefore the average woman must watch constipation at the time of the period very carefully. The basic means of controlling constipation have been discussed in books, articles, magazines, and newspapers. Essentially, they are:

1. The formation of a habit at a regular time. This is the most important aspect of proper bowel function, and it cannot be overemphasized.
2. The inclusion of roughage in the diet—perhaps best illustrated by the phrase a salad or fruit every day.
3. Avoidance of constipating foods. This includes English muffins, sandwiches, cheese, and heavy starches such as macaroni. It might be pointed out, too, since many Americans eat sandwiches for lunch, that one means of avoiding the constipating effect of sandwiches is always to use something in the sandwich with which lettuce may be combined.
4. The use of some naturally laxative food such as prune juice, apple juice, grapefruit juice, or for some people, grapefruit or prunes or bran.

The avoidance of fluid retention. This is done by maintaining a low sodium diet a week before the period and, thus, avoiding a good deal of congestion as well.

Making use of specific exercises, such as the knee-chest exercises, as may be suggested by a physician.

Medications. One medication may be beneficial for some and detrimental to others. It takes trial and error on the part of both the physician and the patient to find the right medication or combinations of medication for each particular woman.

It is the considered opinion of most gynecologists that narcotics have no place in the treatment of pelvic congestion or menstrual cramps.

Occasionally, menstrual pain rather than menstrual cramps is associated with some pathology, some actual disease in the pelvis, for example, infection, inflammation, abscess, endometriosis, or twisted ovarian cysts. Menstrual pain is different from menstrual cramps in that it is not generally in the midline and the pain is usually constant rather than colicky. These problems, of course, can be treated only after investigation.

A very few women have true menstrual cramps which are severe enough to make them "pelvic cripples," that is, they lose two, three, or four days of work or schooling every month. Surgery is sometimes indicated here, and in many of these cases it can be beneficial, but the use of such surgery is not common. There are tests, which indicate whether or not the expectation of success is justified before the surgery is performed.

Tampons vs. Napkins

Discussion of menstruation inevitably brings us to a discussion of the use of tampons and napkins. Both are quite satisfactory, and under given circumstances one may be more convenient than the other. The napkins, of course, have been used traditionally; tampons are of more recent popularity. Napkins have a proven adequacy in most situations, and for those who like to be ultra-scientific and overly-cautious napkins obviously have no effect upon the neck of the womb or the vagina. They may be used without difficulty by the unmarried, the very young, and the very old. They have disadvantages in warm weather, in swimming, and in certain other activities in which they are either uncomfortable or actually irritating.

It has been said that tampons are more comfortable and

more easily employed and disposed of. They can be used in such activities as swimming, for example, without producing irritation of the lips of the front passage or irritation of the hair follicles. Most authorities, however, agree that it is probably unwise for a girl under sixteen to use tampons. She is apt to be insufficiently aware of herself and her organs to insert the tampons easily and properly. Since this area is somewhat tender and sensitive, her first experience with her own genital organs may be a painful one, and this may hamper her psychologically in future life. Furthermore, she may have difficulty at such an age in inserting the tampon through the hymen. There is also a possible danger, although many people consider this rather inconsequential, that in manipulating the tampon in order to insert it properly, the young, immature girl may inadvertently discover herself and the sensitivity of the area and may be introduced to the habit of masturbation.

Very elderly women who sometimes have an irritating discharge which is associated with the changes in the vagina due to age generally are advised against using tampons. The difficulty here is not one associated with the tampons, but with the elderly person, who may forget to remove it. This leads to rather unhappy results. The elderly person forgets the tampon and a foul, odorous discharge occurs which creates a real problem to everyone in the home and is aggravated by the fact that the odor may be obvious to everyone except the user. This danger is also applicable to pledgets of cotton, which elderly people tend to use if tampons are not available.

Very occasionally, a woman who has a heavy flow on the first or second day finds that tampons are not adequate, and she chooses to use a napkin as well. However, in the average girl with the average flow, tampons have certainly proved themselves adequate.

The problem is always raised whether or not tampons

should be employed if a woman is having a bloody, irritating, itchy, colored, or profuse discharge. The quick answer is always no; tampons should not be used under these circumstances. The answer is correct. Not because the tampon necessarily would do any further harm other than to make the person who has this uncomfortable discharge comfortable and, therefore, prolong the time when the patient would seek advice, but because there is some disease in the cervix or the vagina, the neck of the womb or the front passage, which requires attention and, therefore, regardless of whether tampons are used or not such a woman requires investigation to determine the origin of such a discharge.

Another frequent question is whether or not intercourse should take place during menstruation. There are, of course, certain religious strictures and racial customs which forbid intercourse during the period. The Catholic religion does not forbid it. From a broader, factual view of the matter, we should remember that although men and women may be aroused to sexual excitement and sexual appetite at almost any time under fortuitous circumstances, there are two times in the course of a month when every woman is to some degree more easily aroused sexually than at other times. These are at menstruation and ovulation. Women themselves will frequently volunteer that they "feel more passionate" at these times. Since a woman often has a drive or desire for the act of love at the time of menstruation, this whole question can raise a problem within a home. If a woman is very uncomfortable due to menstrual cramps or premenstrual tension on the first day, or if, as may be her custom on the first or second day, she is having a heavy flow, then for esthetic or practical reasons, intercourse may have to be foregone. Similarly, on a psychological basis, if a woman has been brought up to believe that she is dirty, unclean, or a thing apart because she is having her menstrual period, she may have great difficulty in bringing herself to the act of love with her husband during menstruation.

The practical answer to the question, therefore, is if the couple have an earnest desire for the act of love at the time of menstruation, and the girl is not uncomfortable, and there is no esthetic barrier to the act itself, then there is no reason why the couple may not satisfactorily have intercourse at the time of menstruation and both thoroughly enjoy it. The only point is that the act should not be persistently, repetitiously, and exclusively performed during menstruation. Theoretically, persistent, repetitious coitus during the menstrual flow might contribute to a type of pelvic disease, but this has never been proven.

The Douche

The douche is simply a treatment (not a daily or weekly ritual) which has been used for many years as a means of correcting infection or inflammation in the neck of the womb and the vagina. "Hot" douches have a secondary function, getting heat to the pelvic organs. All nurses in the course of their training have to learn how to give a douche properly and satisfactorily to assist in the management of internal infections or inflammation. But the douche, as such, is becoming an outmoded form of therapy; most schools of nursing find it difficult, if not impossible, to train a student nurse in the proper way of giving a douche because there are not enough patients in the hospital who require a douche.

It is regrettable that so many women still feel a douche is necessary to cleanse themselves, for the fact is the vagina is one of the most efficient self-cleansing organs in the body. However, there are always two ways of doing anything—

right and wrong—and the douche is no exception. The wrong way of taking a douche is to sit over a toilet using a bulb syringe. This is less time-consuming than the proper method described below; unfortunately, among other things, it violates Newton's law of gravity and the pleats in the vagina cannot be properly cleansed.

A proper douche, that is, one taken to cleanse the vagina and the cervix of secretions which are the result of inflammation and infection, must be taken either while reclining in a bathtub or on a bedpan. The reason for this is very simple. The wall of the vagina is like an accordion-pleated skirt, and to cleanse the vagina properly, it must be filled to the extent that the folds or pleats in its wall are flattened out so the areas between the pleats can be properly washed. This can be accomplished only if the woman is lying flat. In this position, the vagina is at a forty-five degree angle to the woman's body; it will fill up with the solution and the entire vaginal wall and cervix can be washed properly. This is a time-consuming business. The patient must first boil water, mix the solution, and fill a fountain. She must then undress and, while in the bath, with the hose from the fountain in the vagina, fill the vagina repeatedly so that the proper amount of fluid irrigates the vagina as prescribed by the physician. It usually requires twenty minutes, at least, to do this properly. Since the contact of the douche fluid with the vaginal wall is of such short duration, it is frequently advised that the douche be taken two, three, or four times a day. This is frequently difficult, if not impossible, for a woman to do, particularly if she has three or four children. This is why the douche is becoming more and more unpopular.

There are also innumerable improper solutions to use in taking a douche. The normal secretions of the vagina are mildly acid. When the vagina is infected, its secretions are generally found to be strongly alkaline. Common infections like trichomonas and monilia are generally found associated with such strongly alkaline media. So, an alkaline solution has little or no place in the use of a douche. This means, for example, that such common household remedies as baking soda should not be employed in the vagina. Similarly, many of the preparations which are recommended for inclusion in douche solutions, however sweet-smelling and refreshing they may appear to be, have a rather doubtful value in any effective douche.

There are available today medicated jellies, ointments, suppositories, and tablets which are more effective in the treatment of infection or inflammations of the neck of the womb or the vagina. They are much easier to employ, require seconds to use, and their value in time-contact (that is, prolonged contact of their medication in the vaginal wall) is measured in hours rather than minutes, which makes them infinitely more effective than the douche.

A douche after intercourse has been recommended by some people in the past for contraceptive and for cleansing purposes. As a contraceptive, it is a mechanical interference with the normal marital act; it is considered unnatural and, therefore, immoral. It might also be pointed out that it is probably the most inefficient and untrustworthy form of contraception yet devised by man.

As a method of cleansing the vagina, it is unnecessary. As already indicated, the vagina is a remarkably self-cleansing organ. The only care that is needed after the normal marital relations is the use of some tissues for external purposes and external cleanliness the following morning. In any case, nothing as mundane as a douche should be attractive to a couple after they have loved each other in the way that a kind Providence has ordained for them.

12

Miscarriage and Infertility

Miscarriage is a real and human experience that is fairly common. As a matter of fact, almost any woman who gets pregnant often enough will eventually have a miscarriage. Unfortunately, much misinformation about miscarriage has been disseminated, and it has caused untold unhappiness among women who earnestly desire to have a normal baby.

The exact cause of miscarriage is not known. However, no one specific item can be pinned down as the basic cause, although we are fairly certain that the parents' actions or lack of them have nothing to do with the causes of miscarriage. A miscarriage is considered nature's way of getting rid of a bad egg. Studies of miscarriage material brought to the hospital and sent to the laboratory for investigation indicate that the vast majority of miscarriages contain a fault in the development of the egg itself (that is the fetus), the surrounding membranes, bag of water, or the afterbirth.

These faulty developments involving the embryo or the after-birth are incompatible with life. There is much reason to believe that on the first day a woman starts to bleed, the pregnancy, in most cases, has already been dead for a matter of days or even weeks. Of course, not every woman who bleeds early in pregnancy miscarries; and those who don't miscarry generally produce normal babies at term. The present difficulty is detecting at the time of the bleeding early in a pregnancy which patient will miscarry and which will carry on to a normal term pregnancy. There is no accurate test at this time to help us.

It is conservatively estimated that well over a half million miscarriages occur yearly in the United States. Science is still trying to find a way to stop this enormous loss of fetal life. Various methods have been tried to prevent miscarriage; none of them have proven completely satisfactory. The use of several kinds of hormones and vitamins, psychotherapy, and complete bed rest have all individually and collectively proven unsatisfactory. More recently, the theory that miscarriages are a genetic disturbance involving abnormal numbers or types of chromosomes and therefore are the result of abnormal pregnancies has been postulated by research groups. Then again, the more exotic tests involving skin grafts between the mother and father is based upon a not entirely unsupported assumption that a mother who is having miscarriages, especially if she repeatedly loses what appear to be normal pregnancies, has become sensitized to her husband's tissue. Since a woman's pregnancies are derived, at least in part, from her husband's tissues, the sensitization, it is reasoned, crosses over to the baby who is rejected by the mother's tissues as one to whom she has become sensitized. Insofar as the control of miscarriage is concerned, there is more serious consideration being given to the idea of concentrating on the general health of the couple or the local health of their reproductive tracts *before* the pregnancy occurs. This may turn out to be more important in the salvation or prevention of miscarriages than anything now on the horizon.

On a supposition that most women will eventually have a miscarriage, it is perhaps wise to outline the certain things that should be done. These will depend upon the advice given by a person's individual physician who, after all, is the only person who knows the patient and her problem.

1. Most physicians want to be called if the patient is having bleeding, cramps, low backache, or all of these things combined.
2. If the bleeding becomes excessive and large clots are passed (the size of a lemon or greater), in most instances the patient will be admitted to a hospital.
3. If the patient miscarries, some care must be given to the material that has been passed. If the patient miscarries in the hospital, generally the material that is passed is sent to the laboratory for diagnosis and study for cause. Miscarriage material is always, of course, baptized conditionally and this is taken care of in the hospital if the patient is there. Should the miscarriage take place at home, then the problem of its management rests, naturally, upon the shoulders of the wife or the husband. Should the material that is passed obviously be a pregnancy, then the material should be baptized conditionally either by pouring water over it or by dipping it in water while saying, "If you are capable of being baptized, I baptize you in the name of the Father, and of the Son, and of the Holy Spirit." If there is a sac present and recognizable, the sac must be opened prior to the actual baptismal ceremony. In most cases, the

sac contains largely clear fluid and no embryo can be seen even when it is opened. This is typical of most miscarriages. Once the material has been conditionally baptized, it should then be placed in rubbing alcohol and taken with the patient to the hospital; or, if the physician should decide that the patient is not bleeding enough to go to the hospital but elects to treat the miscarriage at home, the material should still be brought to the hospital or to the doctor's office from where it can go to a laboratory and be examined.

If the material that has been passed is not recognizable, it is always a simple matter to conditionally baptize it and place it in a clean jar and cover it with rubbing alcohol, which is available in most homes. Alcohol is the only material commonly found in most homes which can preserve tissue that has been passed so that it can be taken to the laboratory and examined with some chance of discovering what type of tissue it is and what the problem is. Sometimes patients are concerned that the material fixed in the alcohol and taken to a laboratory or hospital will turn out to be a clot. This does happen, but in any case, no harm has been done and the clot is easily recognized in the laboratory as such and consequently is not processed. The important features of the whole problem of miscarriage are, first, that it can happen to anyone and generally does. Second, if the bleeding is heavy with the passage of large clots the patient most commonly will go to the hospital. Third, any material that is passed should be saved. If it is discovered to be obviously a blood clot, this can be thrown away. Any other material should be conditionally baptized, placed in rubbing alcohol, and taken either to a physician's office or laboratory of a hospital for investigation.

Much has been said in women's lay literature and the lay press in general about the habitual aborter. The term habitual aborter was devised by a man who made a study of miscarriages in the British Isles about forty years ago. He concluded from his survey that any woman who had had three consecutive miscarriages was an habitual aborter and, therefore, not likely to give birth to a normal, full-term child. This aspect of his work has been repeated on six or seven different occasions without confirmation. The term habitual aborter remains. If a woman has had three miscarriages she and her husband certainly should try to discover the cause. But their situation is not hopeless.

It is true that if a woman falls into a pattern of having miscarriages, it is more difficult for her to break into the pattern of having a full-term living child. It is an awkward problem for the medical profession because we simply don't realize or understand the cause or causes behind the repeated aborter. It is a tragic problem for the individual because it is she who has the repeated frustration of motherhood. There is no reason to believe, however, that abortion is a personal characteristic of a woman simply because she has had so many.

One final word. One of the unhappiest habits peculiar to humans is the constant attempt to find someone to blame. Nowhere in medicine is this more apparent than in miscarriage, and the target is always the mother. So we must emphasize a few facts about miscarriages:

1. Most pregnancies are dead for days or even weeks before the start of the bleeding which culminates in the miscarriage.
2. Most miscarriages represent the loss of a "bad egg."
3. There is no known connection between the everyday actions of the parents and the miscarriage.

4. It is extremely difficult to disturb a normally implanted pregnancy.

Infertility

Everyone who discusses infertility, particularly within the confines of a doctor's office, hopefully speaks of that type of infertility which is potentially correctible. It is estimated that 40 per cent of infertile couples can be given assistance that will enable them to fulfill the primary purpose of marriage. The problem of infertility, however, is real; it is reasonably common and somewhat more serious than the local conversations in the bridge clubs would have you believe. In the United States, approximately one marriage in six is an infertile marriage. Furthermore, probably one pregnancy in eight will miscarry. The most common clinical entity American obstetricians and gynecologists see is pregnancy or the accidents of pregnancy; the second most common problem they see is the inability of a woman to become pregnant.

A marriage is considered infertile when pregnancy has not occurred after a year of intercourse with no attempt to avoid pregnancy. Infertility may occur in different ways:

1. Couples have no success in initiating pregnancies.
2. A couple may find that it is easy for them to initiate a pregnancy, but that the woman cannot bring the pregnancy to term.
3. Repeated stillbirths at or near term (fortunately rare) haunt some couples.
4. "One-child sterility." Here the couple usually rather quickly produce one prodigy, but no pregnancies occur thereafter. This can be one of the most difficult types

of infertility to solve; often the longer the interval between the birth of the one child and the search for another, the more difficult is the solution.

These problems are generally referred to under the common heading of *relative infertility*. *Absolute infertility*, or sterility, exists where for cogent and usually anatomical or mechanical reasons pregnancy is not at all possible, for example, if a woman's tubes are completely blocked due to an old infection or adhesions, or she is not ovulating, or the male is not producing any sperm. An odd type of sterility is the one in which repeated investigation shows no reason in either partner why pregnancy should not take place; nevertheless, since the couple cannot conceive, their sterility turns out to be, de facto, absolute—pregnancy simply does not occur in these people. Fortunately, this group is rather small, but such failure causes great frustration in the physician and great anguish in the couple.

Many engaged couples worry about producing a baby in the first year of married life. Undoubtedly some of them have good reasons for not wanting a pregnancy early in their marriage. However, every couple should think seriously about the matter of infertility. It might behoove them, at least in some instances, to prove first of all that they can have a child before they take strenuous steps to insure that they don't.

The most precious thing that a woman takes into her pregnancies, apart from general health, is her age. The younger she is when she becomes a mother, the easier usually is the birth process and the difficult task of child-rearing for both mother and child. Furthermore, with young people in love the human element is so apt to creep into any method of limiting children that there is considerable ground for thinking that if a couple in the first year of married life have not produced a pregnancy, their success in avoiding pregnancy may very well be due to the fact that pregnancy is not possible for them. Certainly it is not unreasonable to assume that couples who make rhythm, or any form of child limitation, work for two or three or four years probably owe their success to a basic infertility.

If a couple has produced no children in four or five years and on investigation the cause of the infertility is found to be, for example, the presence of fibroid tumors of the womb (a not uncommon condition in a woman over thirty), then it is not unreasonable to suppose that the fibroids *have become worse during the last four or five years of waiting.* This brings up two points:

1. *The premarital examination* can detect such things as fibroids and many other, though not all, conditions which may affect the health and fertility of the partners at the beginning of marriage.
2. A delay of three or four years before an infertility investigation often is attributable to family or friends. The usual statement is "don't push it; if God wants you to have children you'll have them." This is a simple and pious declaration of faith; however, it ignores the practical faith to be found in the statement, "The Lord helps those who help themselves."

Nature recognizes that man is a relatively infertile animal. Each time he makes love with his wife, the husband produces up to 400,000,000 sperm in order to insure pregnancy and thus, the perpetuation of the human race. Of course, only one sperm can normally penetrate an egg. We have seen, furthermore, that the average woman may produce only about ten eggs a year, thus, she may not be fertile on more than ten days in the course of a year. When the sperm are placed in the vagina they are placed in a medium which is normally somewhat acid. The secretions of the womb itself and at the neck of the womb are alkaline, and the sperm are capable of finding and enjoying much healthier living in an alkaline media; therefore, they are drawn to the alkaline media of the cervix. They then swim up through the uterus and into the Fallopian tube, where the hair-like structures in the cells in the lining of the tube set up a flow of fluid that is found in the wall of the tube and push the sperm forth to meet the egg. The egg is a fairly large cell, about 1/200″ in size, and just barely visible to the naked eye. It is conditioned to receive one sperm. Under normal conditions, the sperm penetrates the surface of the egg, and the head of the sperm enters the substance of the egg and fertilizes the egg itself. The egg and the sperm normally meet in the tube, and, thus, the pregnancy is begun. The egg, on fertilization, immediately proceeds to grow, the cells growing in doubling multiples.

The egg rapidly becomes larger. If a narrow portion of the tube prevents the growing egg from going down through the tube and into the womb, we have obstruction. The egg begins to grow in a location where it is not intended to—the tube. This is a fertilized egg, or pregnancy, which is "out of place." A tubal pregnancy, as this particular instance is called, is probably the most common form of ectopic (out of place) pregnancy. If the egg continues to grow in the tube, it will eventually erode through the wall of the tube and perforate it. A surgical emergency thus arises which generally requires the removal of the tube, or at least part of it. Other types of ectopic pregnancy arise should the pregnancy be fertilized and start to develop in the ovary, or the abdominal cavity, or any place outside the tube or the womb. However, the meeting of the egg by the sperm in the tube is the first major step of every normal pregnancy.

If the tube is normal, and the egg does not become obstructed (as is usually the case), then the egg proceeds down the tube into the womb and burrows by means of special cells on the outside of the egg into the lining of the womb, where it has a home for nine months. This is the beginning story of all normal pregnancies.

Examinations for Infertility

An infertility investigation should check as many of the normal steps in pregnancy as possible. Briefly stated, it would include after a thorough general physical examination of both partners:

1. Examinations and tests to determine that the neck of the womb is healthy; that is, that there is no inflammation and that the mucus produced by the cervix is normal.
2. A determination whether or not the woman is producing eggs regularly, and by means of the temperature charts a pinpointing of the exact time when she does produce the egg.
3. Investigation to determine if the girl is producing a good bed within her womb into which a tiny pregnancy can burrow and grow. This is done by an endometrial biopsy, which may be done in the office. Within a few hours after the onset of menstruation, or within a day or two before the expected menstruation, an instrument is passed into the womb and tiny strips of the lining of the womb are obtained to prove ovulation and to determine if the bed is a good one and is showing the effects of good hormone levels.
4. Investigation to determine if the male is producing sperm. We also are interested in the number of sperm and whether or not they are alive, and even more particularly, whether or not they are alive after they have

been deposited in the vagina of the wife. This test may *not* be done by masturbation or withdrawal at the time of intercourse. The testing of the validity of the sperm may be done by one of several means. The most common are:

    A. The Huhner Test. Within a few hours after normal intercourse, the woman goes to the doctor's office and the remaining sperm in her vagina are examined. There are certain theoretical drawbacks to this test, yet most of us who use it extensively have rarely found a urologist, on subsequent examination of the male, to draw a conclusion which is contrary to the one drawn after a Huhner Test. It has two distinct advantages: (1) It is completely moral; (2) It tells us the condition and activity of the sperm *under conditions in which the sperm must do its work.*

    B. The male, after intercourse, goes to a doctor's office and the remaining sperm are stripped from the urethra and examined for motility and form. It is even possible to get a reasonably good approximation of the number of sperm produced.

    C. The use of the perforated condom. The male wears a condom in intercourse which has a hole in it. The hole allows some sperm to enter the vagina and thus maintain the integrity of the marital act; at the same time, enough sperm are collected for the urologist to examine. This method is usually distasteful to the couple and barely adequate for the physician.

5. Investigations to determine if the tubes are clear. These are office examinations. This is commonly done by one of two methods, but occasionally both are required. The first is to pass carbon dioxide by means of a machine

through the tubes to see if they are open and under what pressure the gas may pass through the tubes. If there is any question of the tubes being blocked, then the tubes are injected with a dye which will show up under X rays and the X-ray pictures are taken while the dye is in the tubes. This tells us not only if the tubes are closed but at what point they may be closed. It also indicates any disease in the tubes and in the womb itself.

These are the commonly performed, basic, necessary tests in the determination of infertility. There are many others. Some are given for special indications or research.

Adoption

Before leaving the problem of infertility, a few words about adoption are in order. A certain percentage of all patients with an infertility problem eventually must resort to adoption. Many doctors talk about adoption even at the first visit for an infertility investigation if the couple have been married for three years or more, or are in the twenty-five to thirty-year group or older. There are four good reasons for this:

1. If the couple have been married for three years or more, as already indicated, solving their problem may be a little bit more difficult than the couple whose infertility dates back only one year. This does not mean, however, that their case is hopeless or that they should be discouraged if they have been married for three years without children.
2. Sometimes, in a particular case, an adequate investigation of both partners may require six months to a year.

3. In most communities, because there are so many infertile couples looking for babies to adopt, it may take as long as *two years* for a couple to get a baby.

4. In most communities a newborn (in adoption this generally means a child of three or four months old) usually will not be given to a couple if the woman is thirty-five or older and the man is forty-two or over. These are ground rules subject to the opinions and experiences of the various adoption agencies throughout the country.

It should be pointed out that before an application for adoption will be processed, most adoption agencies require a statement from a physician or physicians indicating that a couple have been investigated and found to be unable to have their own children. Doctors are frequently asked their opinion about the advisability of adoption. This is a question which requires a sage to answer; however, it can be answered honestly at least and in general terms.

1. In most communities, the health, development, and habits of babies are studied, usually for three or four months, before they may be adopted. The environmental, and to some extent the hereditary, backgrounds of the parent or parents are known to the adoption agencies. An earnest attempt is made to see that every couple who receives a baby gets a normal one, and so far as possible, a baby with the same national and racial background and even the same color hair and eyes.

2. An earnest effort is made by the adopting agencies to determine if the couple can afford to give the child the basic opportunities of a home and education. An even more earnest effort is made by the agency to try to insure the fact that the child will receive love.

3. In my own experience, and I believe the experience of most doctors, particularly in the last twenty years, the

process of adoption has been notably successful in building good homes and in supplying good parents to unfortunate children who want only one thing—love.

If I were to summarize the problem of adoption, I think I would refer you to a book entitled *Eddy and the Archangel Mike* which was popular a few years ago. In this book the Archangel Mike is talking to "The Boss" about a poor, harassed editor in Texas. In substance the Archangel Mike tells "The Boss" that it has always been His policy to give everyone down there one "big break." Michael apparently is urging that this poor editor is ready for his "big break."

I think that all doctors who come to grips with the problem of adoption see striking evidence of the Hand of Providence. We feel that any thinking person must wonder why Divine Providence allows so many children to be born unhappily out of wedlock; and then one's attention is drawn to the number of people who desperately want children and find themselves afflicted with infertility. It may be somewhat overly sentimental for a scientific person to say this, but it does seem that the Hand of God is particularly visible in the situation, and with so many people waiting with so much love to offer to a child, it seems as though the Lord decided to give these poor little ones their "big break" early in life.

13

For Better or for Worse

Those who enter into a Catholic marriage should bring with them love, determination, and a capacity for real effort. No one suggests that to live a Catholic life is easy—it's just profitable, wholesome, and important. It is a life in which sacrifice must be endured for loved ones and for Christ. It requires self-discipline and a spirit of self-denial. The love must be lived, and a solemn word given must be kept.

On the wedding day the promise is made "to have and to hold, from this day forward, for better, for worse, for richer, for poorer, in sickness and in health until death do us part." It is solemn, specific, and permanent. Perhaps the suggestion is not without merit which urges that the engaged couple read the marriage ceremony every day until the wedding. Clearly, the most important decision in marriage is the first one. The selection of the partner will determine if "for better, for worse" will be a difficult labor of love or a taste of hell. If each partner is warm and honest and stable, if there is

reciprocity of feeling, if both are working on the same definition of love—then the person *is* the thing and considerations
of wealth, poverty, time, illness, or health are secondary.

One of the nice things about marriage is that the good
or successful marriage is always the silver lining in any
clouded life. A good marriage makes it quite easy, comparatively speaking, for either member of the partnership or
both together to weather the same crisis, such as death in the
family, separation, war, or illness. The sadness, the anguish,
and even the depression attended by any of these events
draws a couple closer together; they have discovered their
unity and have achieved an ability for self-expression as two
people enjoying a common life. This unity is not only of
purpose but of action in the process of living and in the
management of success and hardship. In any successful marriage, the couple are comrades in arms, so to speak. This
requires a leisurely companionship between two people—
husband and wife—which makes possible excellent communication with a minimum of words.

In the ensuing pages we will explore some of the situations and changes which inevitably enter and alter lives. We
will discuss several problems common to most couples, such
as money, working wives, and special problems such as
alcoholism—not with exhaustive authority but with the view
that the healthiest way to solve a problem is to accept it,
that God, love, ingenuity, and determination will help you
find the answer.

Money and Budgets

One of the most common problems in marriage is the
management of money. Now, to try to spend the money in
another man's pocket is the epitome of folly. For a member

of the medical profession to indulge in any definitive comments on basic home economics problems would be grossly presumptuous, so a few generalizations are all I will permit myself, generalizations based on personal experience and observations. It is worthy of note that most "budget experts" of my acquaintance feel they can help newly-weds best after three to six months of marriage—after they've had an opportunity to settle down and define their plans, preferences, and prejudices.

The general advice which for years has been given to travelers is intriguing, correct, and, I believe, not completely inappropriate for newly-weds:

1. "Carefully prepare a list of the clothing and other properties which you feel you will need on your journey. When this is done—and carefully—cut the list in half."

2. "Estimate as professionally as you can and with a generous margin of safety, how much money you will need for everyday living—then double it."

Much of the equipment, furniture, and other properties which you feel are essential for your home might better be selected after a second look and a third thought after you take over a house. The necessity for an item which may last throughout much of your married life—a rug, for example—might never be in doubt, but the type of rug might be better selected after a little home building.

Sometimes it is worth considering the purchase, prior to marriage, of perhaps one luxury item even at the expense of a necessity. Thus, a really fine camera or camera projection equipment to preserve happy memories might be purchased instead of an electric dish washer. The thinking here (which is sound for perhaps one item, but utterly irresponsible when applied to a list of items) is that after marriage sacrifices are usually readily and regularly made to obtain a necessity (dish washer) but are impatiently and rather inconstantly made for a luxury (camera).

Few people realize how much ready cash is needed in the home until they've established one. Every woman eventually learns that the stretching qualities of the dollar are best appreciated when the key in the lock opens the door to *her* home. Then she usually expects it to stretch more than it will. Major fixed expenses—rent or mortgage, light, heat, and car insurance—are readily ascertained. The difficult decisions involve which major items must be cut (different house, smaller car) in order that the more fluid but daily and insistent expenses be met.

Budgets are made for two people in a family, and their success depends upon cooperation and agreement. A budget that is drawn up by one spouse and insisted upon for both supplants the rope in the domestic tug of war.

After the necessities of life have been accounted for, there are a few items which are perhaps best called "essentials for successful family living" or "taking care of the family":

1. Adequate life insurance for the breadwinner.
2. Health and accident insurance—Blue Cross, Blue Shield, *and/or* another reputable type of health and accident policy. Be sure to examine such policies completely— what they *will and will not cover*—before you sign. These policies have to cover some items which are difficult to insure against and some, for example, pregnancy, which are really not insurable. They usually offer coverage on these items, but the benefits are necessarily fixed. Find out what they are. Homes without health and accident insurance are desperately tried in the face of illness today.
3. A savings account—*however small*—at least in the beginning of marriage, sets up the saving habit. This may

later graduate to stocks and bonds, but *if it does not* the savings habit can help people to accumulate a surprising amount of money in even ten years.

4. Most people realize that the home they make after marriage will probably not be their permanent "castle," especially as children come along.

If their first home is rented, then their savings perhaps should be larger in preparation for the purchase of their home.

In addition to budget matters, legal matters associated with future family problems involve:

1. The question of joint bank accounts—whether or not they are desirable in the state where you live. Similarly, joint ownership of property.

2. Wills. The last will and testament, however annoying or depressing to think about, can be very important for the future of a family. All parents should make one out.

These problems should be discussed with an attorney.

Under the heading of money matters, newly-weds regularly think in terms of borrowing money. Borrowing money should not be undertaken lightly. It is a serious step and should be reserved for emergencies. There are several sources from which money can be borrowed, and perhaps each one deserves a word of comment—bearing in mind that the comments are made not by an expert in the field of economics or finance but represent the practical attitude of most people.

1. Loan sharks. The only advantage of a loan shark is easy money. The rates of interest are fantastic, reaching many times several hundred per cent greater than the amount of money borrowed. Stay away from them.

2. Loan companies. Again, the money is easily acquired, but the rate of interest is usually very high.

3. Friends and relatives. No hard and fast answer can be given here, but it is usually unwise to borrow from either friends or relatives. After all, when you borrow money, you assume a just debt and the repayment should be personal, business-like, and regular. Dealings with friends and relatives are usually most unbusiness-like, resulting in the borrower developing a bad habit and the lender a bad attitude.

4. Advance on salary. For short-term loans of small sums of money, and in an emergency, it is useful. It is not recommended as a regular practice nor for large sums of money because it actually amounts to asking the employer to transact serious business in an unbusiness-like way. It also causes the most human employer to wonder about the fiscal habits of the employee.

5. Banks. Banks are good sources of credit. The rates of interest are not exorbitant, and a judicious banker will try to dissuade the borrower from obtaining more money than he can pay back within a reasonable time. Banks require collateral and regular payments.

6. Credit unions. A well-run credit union is an excellent source for borrowing money by the employee. The rate of interest is somewhat lower than the bank's, and if the person is gainfully and regularly employed, no collateral is necessary. There is a limit to the amount of money that may be borrowed, and, in business-like fashion, a credit union will take steps to protect its money.

Many other problems and special considerations will occur to individual couples. Perhaps most important is that a check list, including the budget, be made out and all of the items freely discussed at regular intervals, seeking legal or economic advice where necessary. In this way decisions will be made with unity and care. Husband and wife can help plan for the future, and both can understand the necessity for sacrifices to attain those plans. Sometimes such sacrifices involve the loss of the family car (a real blow to the male especially); sometimes a decision is made to have the wife work. This brings up a special problem in family living.

The Working Wife

It is probable that at all times in history wives have had to work outside the home. But it is estimated that in the United States since 1940 there have been more wives working than at any other time or place in history. Many women took jobs to support the war effort and did magnificently. Some liked it and others did not; some found it easy and stimulating and others found expression for hidden talents; some found it unusually lucrative. But all, particularly professional people, discovered, even with a lay-off of several years occasioned by family responsibilities, that there were opportunities in this land—even for women. Although the number of working wives during the 1940's was considerably higher than now, it is estimated that even today, one out of every five or six women working in this country is a working wife.

After the war, a new type of working wife appeared on the horizon—the wife of the student. The war veteran who went to college partially subsidized by the government was at an age where he wanted a wife and family as well as an education, and frequently his wife had to work at least part-time to help support the family.

The two people involved should discuss this problem thoroughly and decide upon a course of action which is mutually agreeable. Their discussion should cover all the possibilities, including their plan of action should the wife become pregnant or ill. What will they do should the task of maintaining a home, a family, and a job prove to be emotionally or physically exhausting for the woman? Both partners must understand what kind of a sacrifice is being made (that it is temporary and for a worthwhile purpose goes without saying). The wife must realize that her husband's pride is on the line; he is bound to resent the fact that the maintenance of his home depends on his beloved. The husband must realize that the average wife wants a family life, and that this is a very considerable part of her burden when she assumes the double task of maintaining a home and being the homemaker as well.

This situation requires sacrifice on the part of both for a common good. It requires inventiveness and discipline to seek the proper and best path to their goals; to make do with the least available; to maintain honor, a sense of humor, and a level-headedness while sacrificing comfort, hobbies, and sources of entertainment.

All this, of course, can be done well within the Christian concept of marriage provided at the same time both partners realize that the primary responsibilities of marriage involve the responsibility of husband and/or wife to the opposite partner and their mutual responsibilities to their children. If they have children and the family life itself is being sacrificed for a laudable ambition, then the ambition must bow to a revision of their plans. If there are children in the home, the children must have the attention of their mother whether it be for assistance with school work or the development of family discipline and honor. A mother's relationship to her own children must be preserved. If the father's directive and protective influence, except for necessary and relatively short periods of time, is to be removed from the family in the pursuit of an ambition, then the ambition itself must be revised as well. In most cases, a working wife represents an economic need on the part of the family. The working wife of modern times works no harder or no less hard than her predecessor of a hundred years ago. The type of work she does is different, and the contribution she makes to the family is neither more nor less tangible; only it is now measured in dollars and cents.

In the past, women made clothes, bedding, and blankets for everyone in the home. She also baked the bread and often processed the meats and did most of the canning and preserving of staples as well. She not only had to do the cleaning (as does her modern counterpart), but she had to make the cleaning materials, such as soap. Today machines and new products relieve the wife of most of this effort and tedious work. Modern appliances, however, cost money. This means that the husband's income necessarily has to be greater to supply artificially those services which in past years were produced by personal effort. The income of any man is limited by the number of hours that he can work and the amount of money that his talents and abilities can command. Because neither of these factors is inexhaustible in any individual, in the home, particularly where there are a number of children, it may be necessary for the wife to become involved in some part-time work. Some women, of course, are not able to work and keep a home. They are capable and efficient housewives, but their abilities are limited to these capacities. This is nothing to be ashamed of.

In the United States it is probable that only the farmer's wife usually does not engage in other types of work. Both the farmer and his wife traditionally have been hard-working people who have always expended their best efforts in accepting the challenge from nature to draw their livelihood from the soil.

In areas near cities of some size, where opportunities for employment are naturally greater, many women undertake full-time employment early in marriage, before the children come along, and after the youngest has reached the age of twelve to fifteen. This illustrates one side of a difference of opinion common among women, regarding working while their families are growing up. These women feel that their families need their undivided attention during the formative years, that their physical presence is an integral and necessary aspect of family life. They will make almost any sacrifice during the formative years of the children to be present for any need.

On the other side of the coin are those women who believe that it is possible and perhaps desirable to work at least part time while the children are growing. Some women with growing children find that part-time work is diversionary; others require release from the pressure of growing children. As a matter of fact, many women, when exposed to different attitudes, ideas, and opinions outside the home at regular intervals bring a fresh approach to the management of family problems and to the development of family attitudes. Such work is usually part-time because a full-time job would take too much time from the children or be too strenuous for the mother. Urgent economic distress within the family, at least on a temporary basis, may make part-time work on the part of the mother the only practical and immediate solution.

Many working wives function as assistants to their husbands in a privately-owned business. For some women this is nerve racking—they feel torn between the needs of the family business and the needs of the family. Others find this type of work very satisfactory because it makes them feel they are making a distinct contribution to the welfare of the home.

It is generally agreed that specially trained people should "keep their hands in" even though the home commitments are great while the children are small. This refers particularly to artists, writers, teachers, and physicians. Most specially trained people need the aesthetic, artistic, and intellectual stimulation which even a few hours a week in their special field affords them. This also keeps them from getting stale and allows them to maintain contact with new developments in what was once their chosen field. And such activity is considered a good example for the children and an additional stimulation intellectually and artistically. Finally, a woman maintains a position in which at the appropriate time she may still make a real contribution to the community, apart from her family.

Some women, of course, are hypomanic—they simply have to be doing something all the time. These women are better when driving themselves because, in the absence of work for themselves, they tend to drive others. Usually women of this type recognize their problem, and they prefer to drive themselves.

The Student Wife

Prior to the war, it was socially unacceptable as well as unusual for a student to be married, but we now find married students at all levels. And in many cases, the student's wife is also a working wife. The married student is here to stay. Many of these marriages work out quite successfully; the people know each other for several years, are convinced of their love for one another, and convince their elders and parents of the same fact. Having seen and heard of the difficulties of long engagements, it is only natural that the youth of today, perhaps more so than the youth of previous generations, desire marriage and education at the same time. If such a course is decided upon by mature individuals with a sense of adult responsibility and an idea of just what they are getting into, they will be prepared to make the necessary plans and sacrifices.

The young person perhaps is more inventive than self-sacrificing, and there are many opportunities for married students to fulfill their happiness and ambition. The more able ones grasp these opportunities. Our concern is for those who have perhaps not discussed or thought out this problem sufficiently—particularly those who feel they must sacrifice their ambition out of necessity, thereby risking developing serious frustrations which can effect their happiness ten years hence.

One of the principal concerns in this situation is delaying pregnancy for one or several years. This can be a legitimate decision and a legitimate desire, but it is usually difficult to maintain. I think the best advice that can be offered to such a couple falls into the following categories:

1. A decision to postpone babies should be reconsidered periodically because, as the Chinese say, no man has yet drunk tomorrow's cup of tea. Within three months, six months, or a year, one's ideas and desires may change quite substantially on this subject. And if they do, both partners must be determined and resigned to accept the new decision and to work within its confines.

2. The couple must be prepared to accept the fact of pregnancy if it should occur despite the best-laid plans of well-intentioned people.

3. They should have an alternative plan, however difficult, however much may be delayed their goal, which allows them to accept their family responsibility and maintain their ambitions at the same time.

4. Should they enter marriage with a plan to postpone, they should carry with them as complete information

about the girl's menstrual cycle for the previous year as is possible to obtain. In this respect, as indicated in the chapter "Limitation of the Family," an interested physician can assist them.

5. They should remember that there is a bright face to danger, that is to say, whatever happens that seems to disturb their plans can be viewed with gloom or as a blessing and a challenge to their inventiveness and determination. The latter attitude has always been that of successful people.

The working wife of a student is generally young, vigorous, enthusiastic—and in love. She maintains the home and pays the bills. She must nurture most carefully her husband's ego and be vigilant against a pregnancy. While he attend classes, visits libraries, writes papers, and studies at home—she works. Rarely do they have time for "social breaks" or entertainment even if they have the money. She works until he gets his degree and, not uncommonly, continues to work while he gets another.

This system is a real test of love—the monotony of effort, effort, effort builds tensions; fear of a pregnancy increases the tension; and several years with no babies may build frustrations and anxieties. Ambition must indeed be made of stern stuff. Love is more than adequate to the task, but it is not easy.

There are human complications. The girl, as we have indicated, may be young, vigorous, enthusiastic, and in love. She is frequently only a high school graduate. It is not our purpose to dwell on such a snobbish thought or pursue all its implications. Let us simply say that, after five or six years of study and two degrees the husband has changed; his vistas have broadened, his interests are new, demanding, and technical. The wife occasionally finds herself married to a stranger with whom communication is limited. I do not wish to imply that this problem is necessarily very common or insoluble; however, it does happen. One answer is for the wife to audit courses on various pertinent subjects for information and a broadening influence rather than for credit. It is perhaps something for more colleges to think about since they can be of immediate help.

Money, budgets, and working wives are matters for real heroism in marriage. Squeezing a budget is a real art and hard work. Sacrifices to the common life are daily. Sometimes the husband and father works two jobs daily—with no end in view. He sacrifices his health, his hobbies, his relaxation and leisure, and his contact with his children for their welfare—and, often to avoid the necessity of his wife working. Such a decision places almost all the load of rearing the children (except for two days a week) on the mother.

Similarly, the working wife and mother has many things to think about. Her physical presence in the home is of the utmost importance where there are children. Leaving the home for any extended period should be done most reluctantly and for most serious reasons.

The working wife of the student deserves special praise. Often she must endure a make-shift home because she does not have time to create anything more; she suffers a loneliness which is accentuated by the "quiet" hours of study and the (frequently) absence of babies; she bears the monotony of working hours and the frustrations of no social life. Here is a young girl in love who married for companionship, health, and home—see what she does *for* her beloved!

Alcoholism

Alcoholism, probably the most common of the so-called special problems, has been described as a disease, the nature of which is unknown and a form of addiction. It has been blamed on the will and on bodily deficiency in the hormonal system or the emotions. Studies of alcohol and alcoholism have been undertaken by sociologists, physicians, pharmacologists, psychiatrists, clergymen, and national and local institutions—and the nature of this tragedy has not yet been determined. But we do know that alcoholism does not commonly happen overnight; whenever it may show most dramatically its unhappiest phase, it has been present in some form for years.

It is obvious that the alcoholic goes through several phases. There is general agreement really only on the first and last phases. The first phase involves normal drinking. The normal drinker takes alcohol to savor good food, to put him right with the world, and to enjoy the company of friends. He takes alcohol as a lesson in gracious and comfortable living, which is within the economic limits of almost any home.

The last phase, the stage of chronic alcoholism, is reserved for those who become so degraded by the excessive use of alcohol that they are in danger of losing or have already lost their jobs, health, and family. The chronic alcoholic seems to be driven by an irresistible craving, which is probably best summarized by noting that, regardless of how long his period of abstinence may be, one week or ten years, he can never become a normal or a social drinker. The first drink sets within him a craving for so much alcohol that he doesn't stop until he is totally sodden.

In between the normal drinker and the alcoholic lie the social drinker and the periodic drinker. The social drinker drinks occasionally to excess when he is out with a group; he rarely says no regardless of how many drinks he has had in a social gathering. He is considered at least a potential alcoholic, and he is at the stage where he is using alcohol for a supposed purpose. Everyone is familiar with the phrase "I gotta have a drink after that" referring to an examination, a funeral, an exciting sports event, an accident, a family crisis—or anything. Again, the expressions "Boy, I *need* a drink" or "That calls for a drink," or "Let's go have a few beers" represent danger signals. It is perhaps true that not everyone who reacts this way or uses such phrases inevitably becomes an alcoholic, but it is equally true that there is grave danger of becoming one.

The periodic drinker is usually merely a type of chronic alcoholic. He is less of a burden to himself and to his family than an alcoholic only in that he apparently is able to master himself for at least short periods of time between drunken periods that may last from days to weeks. He remains a threat to his health but usually represents "only" a severe strain on his livelihood and happiness. This type of alcoholic has been of special interest to some psychiatrists, who believe that this type of alcoholism is at least precipitated by stress situations.

It has been well-established that a certain percentage of chronic alcoholics are actually psychotic. There are among them schizophrenics and manic depressives. Some are unhappy epileptics. Research has also established fairly well that a certain percentage of alcoholics are psychopaths. Some are neurotics of rather severe forms; some are feeble-minded, mentally retarded, or what used to be referred to as sexually tense or frustrated. This term is a carryover from the era in which alcoholics were considered to be the result of sexual incompatibilities within the home. I believe that today no one seriously considers this factor to be responsible for more than a small percentage of alcoholics. Some alcoholics appear to be victims of sheer habit formation with or without the presence of a personality defect. It is this group which is the least understood from the psychiatric point of view.

Perhaps the reason why a "disease" of the will is involved

lies in the fact that the most successful management of the alcoholic to appear on the horizon within this century has been Alcoholics Anonymous. The mechanism of their success is not entirely clear, but there seems no question that Alcoholics Anonymous appeals to the will. As a matter of fact, anyone undertaking to assist an alcoholic always insists, as does Alcoholics Anonymous, that he can be of assistance only if the patient admits to being an alcoholic and wills himself to stop drinking. There are numerous methods of assistance available to the alcoholic. All methods are helpful if the patient will admit he is an alcoholic and has the will to stop drinking.

From where we sit, however, it must be stated in all fairness that within the alcoholic's circle of family and friends, not everybody *really* wants to help him. Not uncommonly, we find situations in which the members of the family don't want to admit that an individual is an alcoholic; they foster within the alcoholic the illusion that he or she is not an alcoholic. This attitude is less frequently seen than formerly, but it is still found with annoying frequency, generally within families who do not want to bear the disgrace of harboring an alcoholic. Even in this day and age, too often doctors are approached by the families of alcoholics with a request for a tranquilizer or sedative which they can take so that "they can live with the alcoholic." Several years of living with an alcoholic can discourage almost anyone, but those close to the alcoholic must never give up in their efforts, which may be quietly if intently pursued, to get the alcoholic to seek help. In most communities, help is available, but *it cannot be emphasized too much that the assistance will be of benefit only if the patient has the will to be assisted.* The help takes many forms, from the pledge, which in the experience of the average doctor rarely helps, to the religious approach of the Matt Talbot Societies, psychotherapy, substitution therapy, antabuse or chemical therapy, hospitalization where needed, and Alcoholics Anonymous.

The family must often reorient itself to assist and manage the alcoholic. This may be as important as anything that is done for the alcoholic. It generally takes the form of family group counseling either under the *auspices of Alcoholics Anonymous or some similar group.* Many Alcoholics Anonymous meetings are open to nonalcoholics and their families, and many Alcoholics Anonymous units have sessions for families and teenagers to help with their problems also. Such sessions often help save family unity and sanity. Interest and quiet determination is often worth more than genius. If the alcoholic is to be helped, he must want help—and his family and friends must genuinely want to help him.

Psychiatric Problems

Psychiatric problems sooner or later seem to touch every family to some degree. This doesn't necessarily mean that psychiatric disease is on the upswing; it is probably the result of the awareness by people of personality changes, actual mental disease, and the availability of assistance for both. It is hoped that the general public is coming of age with regard to mental illness. The average patient who is referred to a psychiatrist these days no longer feels a candidate for a mental institution; instead, the patient emerges from the sessions with the psychiatrist feeling better and convinced that his or her condition is probably more benign than a bleeding duodenal ulcer and not very different. I think it can be stated without much fear of contradiction that the greatest difficulty which physicians have with psychiatric referral is almost always centered with the family, not with the patient. Some years ago I saw a young girl who was obviously in a severe depression, with suicidal tendencies. She pleaded for assistance. I was able to get her an appointment with a psychiatrist within the hour. He concurred that she needed immediate hospitalization, and she herself was willing. However, it was several days before her brother, an educated man holding down a position of great responsibility in the community, could be convinced that a member of his family needed psychiatric care. His argument: No member of the family had ever been in a mental institution. His difficulty was that he was not only ignorant of the advances of modern medicine and modern psychiatry, but he had failed to observe what was happening in his own home.

It is obviously impossible, even if it were desirable, to present a long discussion of psychiatric disease. But speaking as a non-psychiatrist and considering the common problems which are seen in the average practice of obstetrics and gynecology—and, I believe, in medicine as a rule—the following symptoms and conditions should be noted.

Perhaps the most significant symptom is a personality change—a person's mood changes in a sudden and seriously different way than has ever been noted before; or moods in which there is deep, increasing irritability, a negativistic attitude, or loss of a sense of humor. Other symptoms are unusual violence in a person's attitude towards others; unusual sensitivity to criticism, or what a person unreasonably thinks is criticism; sudden suspiciousness and argumentativeness. It should be borne in mind that these may be symptoms of organic as well as psychiatric disease and the patient should see a doctor without delay.

Perhaps the most common psychiatric disorder seen by physicians is depression, in which there is loss of appetite, insomnia, lack of interest, loss of ability to make decisions, and crying without cause. One of the most common symptoms of emotional distress is fear—especially when a person is afraid but is not sure of what he or she is afraid. Then, again, a person may have genuine fears of trivial or very unlikely occurrences; compulsions to do things (some of which may be trivial and others serious); an inability to do common things; anxiety to the point where he or she cannot go into crowds, or can go to the door of the home but not through it; paranoia in which they believe that people are plotting against them or are at least against them; and emotional states in which they turn against those whom they love the most.

Psychiatric help, in general, must be obtained when the problems are depression, suicidal tendencies, disorientation, in which a person doesn't know where he or she is, what time it is, what day it is, or where there is violence. There must be a realization that mental illness is real, but not peculiar. There must be an awareness that most mental illness does not involve psychoses or active insanity and commitment to institutions for life. On the contrary, the bulk of psychiatric patients today are those with fears, compulsions, confusion, and anxieties for which they can get very material assistance.

There are four problems which are constantly inquired about in conferences on marriage which apparently represent real worries to a fair percentage of people about to be married. These are:

1. The problem of the person who should see a psychiatrist or should be in a mental institution and "won't go." There are a number of considerations here. In some families, if a person has to see a doctor, regardless of what type, he or she sees the doctor. These are the families which generally have at least one strong-minded individual who is determined that each member of the family will get whatever care is necessary. But there are families which accept the prospective patient's

answer that he or she won't submit to medical care. I have received this verdict repeatedly, once from a family which at three o'clock in the morning watched one individual break all the furniture in the third floor of a home and drop it out the window. It actually came as a surprise to this family that this patient had to be carried to the hospital. It is a never-ending source of surprise to most of us to see families talk in a rational way to an individual who is quite irrational—and obviously irrational—and expect to get a rational answer.

As for the person who is not psychotic but who does need psychiatric care, the best source of help is the family doctor, who in most cases is able to persuade the patient that he or she should at least see a psychiatrist. The ideal answer in these cases, of course, is for the psychiatrist to make a home visit. There are peculiar and technical difficulties associated with this type of psychiatric practice, and attempts are being made now to solve them by setting up pilot studies of home psychiatric care in an attempt to make the management of this particular type of problem easier.

2. Shock therapy is a subject which constantly provokes questions and discussions. The simplest answer is that shock therapy is no panacea for all types of mental illness and has its value chiefly, and in the opinion of some, only in depression or depressed states. In such situations in which it is of value, it helps the sick individual to function again in society rather quickly and less expensively than other methods. By refinement of anesthesia and other techniques, the physical danger of shock therapy has now been minimized.

3. Psychoanalysis: This treatment is long and expensive, and some families which have had experience with it wonder if the efforts have been worth it. To this we can

only say that psychoanalysis has considerable merit; it it a wonderful investigative tool and in certain long-standing, deeply involved problems of emotional or mental illness involving a basic personality disorder it's probably the best although the longest form of therapy. The more modern tendency seems to be to use analysis at a superficial level for diagnosis and to use whatever form of treatment—shock, psychotherapy, assurance, or drugs—which seems most appropriate for returning the patient most quickly to the community and to proper function. Because it is time-consuming, psychoanalysis in the classic sense could not hope to manage more than a very small percentage of the psychiatric illness around us.

4. Psychiatric problems of the aged are quite common subjects of discussion. These are perhaps more properly called problems of the aged because usually they are associated with arteriosclerosis involving the blood vessels in the brain. It is amazing and inexplicable to us how some people in their sixties and early seventies show signs of early mental deterioration while some of their friends who are ten or fifteen years older are bright, alert, inquisitive, and functioning.

The aging problem is a tragic one for any family to face. A mother or father or both, suddenly or gradually show a personality change which in itself, as viewed by the children who knew them in their prime, is as tragic as the havoc that it sometimes wreaks. The chief symptoms are a loss of recent memory with an apparent turning towards the past. Memory of past events becomes acute and keen, and occasionally, in severe states, the individual reverts thirty or forty years or more to engage actually in conversations with people of his or her childhood. These people often turn night into day—

they sleep in the day and remain awake and disturbed in the night. They may become suspicious and make accusations of all types of dire actions and habits. Not uncommonly, they become quarrelsome and violent and turn against those they love the most. Occasionally this is precipitated by a sudden, abrupt change in environment, as for example, a sudden hospitalization involving a strange environment under tension of illness or surgery with a resulting disorientation. Occasionally a change in environment—moving from one member of a family to another—may have some temporary benefit. It may also make the individual worse and even more paranoid than he had been. In a small percentage of cases the most drastic measure, strangely enough, seems to work best. Occasionally, when the individual is transferred to an old people's home, or to a nursing home, where they are among total strangers, they seem to achieve a new lease on life and, tragically, are only difficult when they are visited by their families.

Since the change is arteriosclerotic and mechanical or organic, there is no medication that helps. Their reaction to drugs and medications is unpredictable and occasionally violent. As a matter of fact, most of these people are likely to become wild, excited, and agitated from drugs which are sedatives for most people. There is no easy answer. It is one of the problems of living and one of the problems of family life and it should be managed according to the best traditions of family responsibility and loyalty which usually have been taught by the individual who is now that last leaf on the tree.

The Careless Use of Drugs

We are not here considering addiction to heroin, marijuana, or opium; we are concerned with beneficial, legitimate drugs and their careless use. We consider alcohol a drug, of course. This is probably the one that is most commonly and carelessly used. Most people have an innate sense of caution about the excessive use of such drugs as codeine, demerol, and morphine. Neither demerol nor morphine is commonly prescribed for the public; codeine is. But fortunately, codeine is a very bitter substance and produces nausea in a fair number of people. So, the careless use of legitimate drugs is more likely to involve the non-narcotic drugs.

Chief among these, of course, is the barbiturate. Barbiturates are the sleeping pills, the luminal family of drugs which are extremely valuable for everything from tension states to hypertension and to which it is rather easy for the careless patient to become accustomed. At one time, we used to place the bromides within the same classification, but these are perhaps not so commonly used nowadays, now that the tranquilizers and similar drugs have come into vogue. It is not too difficult to become habituated to barbiturates when a thing as precious as sleep depends upon their use. If anyone in the family is required to use barbiturates for sleep every night for a month (and this may be quite necessary and legitimate), then some responsible member of the family should check with the person's physician to see if he realizes this and to see what his recommendations are. A person who becomes habituated to barbiturates is usually secretive about it—not uncommonly he has a locked cabinet or locked closet in his room, or he locks the room as he leaves. If he is on a heavy dosage, he may show alternating periods of agitation or sleepiness during the day or a slurring type of speech (which may be mistaken for drunkenness).

A person habituated to barbiturates may have accounts at several drug stores and may take prescriptions from different doctors to different drug stores and keep getting them all refilled. It is not too difficult to become habituated to barbiturates if they are used in large doses especially. They are most commonly employed by physicians to tide a patient over a difficult time in his life or to help him to get some sleep. Even under these conditions, however, the general advice is for the patient to take the drugs for two or three nights to get well-rested and then to see if he can go for two or three nights without the medication. When barbiturates are employed for a condition such as hypertension, they are generally used in very small dosages and several times a day. This is not considered habit-forming and does not usually present any visible reaction either in the patient's activities or in his work; as a matter of fact, the patient is generally not aware of any medication effect at all.

Of even greater concern than the barbiturates are the "pep pills." These are used to manage depression or to cut the appetite of people with a weight problem. When the indications are kept tightly defined within a narrow range of conditions and when the administration of these pills is rigidly controlled, as a rule no difficulty ensues. However, some patients who start on these pills find they feel so well with them that they want to continue long after the doctor has advised them to stop—and this is where trouble starts. This type of pill can induce a type of addiction which is quite harmful to the general health of the individual. Then, too, when the pills are used for any period of several months, even in small dosage, a significant number of patients note a feeling of depression after they stop using the drug. More recently, schizophrenic-type behavior on a temporary basis has been noted following the use of the drug in some people for periods of six months or more. *It cannot be emphasized too strongly that these are potent drugs which have certain dangers that cannot be minimized. They should not be taken indiscriminately.*

One other warning should be posted as often as possible.

Even if you think you know what a drug is, even if you are
sure that you *know* what a drug is—*never take another
person's medication.* Each medication prescribed takes into
account the proper dosage for the proper age, height, weight,
knowledge of the patient's condition, what the contra-indica-
tions for the drug may be, and the possibility of allergic reactions. The selection and use of medications are the function of the physician, not the patient.

Your Marriage Through the Years

Change is one of the inexorable facts of living; each day
and each experience is a change over the previous day's experience. One day one poet bids us awake for the sun has
driven the stars into night; the next day his colleague tells
us that some days must be dark and dreary.

All newly-weds emerge from their original state of idyllic
bliss to find that changes are taking place. They wake up
some morning to attend a wedding of some dear friend and
realize that they are now an old married couple (of two
months). They may scarcely have a chance to try out their
new attitudes before the woman discovers that her menstrual
function has suddenly gone awry and she doesn't feel quite
the same as she used to. Pregnancy is upon them, and parenthood beckons seven months hence. Their interests and their
attitudes change; some go delving into books, some quickly
seek the advice of a physician, others are led astray by misinformation from their friends.

Once the great event has occurred, the wife and mother
finds out to what extent change can affect *her.* She who has
received the adulation of the crowd and the attentions of
the experts is now neglected in favor of the baby—except
when the finger of accusation is pointed at her. Eventually a

new change occurs in which the realization that a family has been born spreads its roseate glow over the three.

Minor changes on an everyday basis—somewhat accentuated at the time of new additions to the family—continue for several years. In the normal course of events, the next great change occurs when the first baby enters school and the parents finally discover themselves to be mature members of the P.T.A.—and are not entirely sure that they like it. Life is no longer simply a question of time marching on; rather the inexorable march of age is now pacing towards them.

Again, a succession of minor changes occur, which require the management of problems varying from school tuition to vacation schedules. The next normal milestone in life is the day when the last child starts school. There is no longer a baby in the house and mother has too much time available. She finds grey hairs and new diversions. She reminds father that his hair is thinning and he needs more exercise.

These changes are all mild. They come in rather rapid succession and they are short-lived. The first really major change that indelibly prints itself upon the minds of the couple is the menopause or the change of life.

The Menopause

The "change of life" is one of the few instances where the colloquial expression seems more accurately to describe a condition than the official medical term, the menopause. Strictly speaking the menopause refers to the stoppage or cessation of a woman's menstrual periods. The expression "change of life" is more accurate because three things are actually involved here: the menstrual periods cease, the ovaries stop functioning to any large extent, and a natural sterility appears. The woman not only no longer has menstrual periods, but she doesn't ovulate, and she cannot get pregnant. These changes come to every woman eventually. But these individual items are of greatest importance to the young woman who has had a simple hysterectomy. The removal of her uterus will certainly stop her periods because the organ from which the menstruum comes has now been removed. She will likewise be sterile since the organ in which a baby can grow, by the same token, has been removed. But with a simple hysterectomy her ovaries are still intact, functioning, and, under normal conditions, will usually continue to function until the normal age when she would have had her menopause anyway. Thus, when she had her hysterectomy, she had a menopause but not a change of life.

On the other hand, if a woman has her womb and her ovaries removed, regardless of her age, she then develops what is called an acute surgical menopause or, more properly, an acute surgical change of life. With her uterus and ovaries removed, she can no longer have periods, she can no longer have babies, and she no longer produces eggs or ovarian hormones in any quantity. Naturally there is no ovarian function.

Since every woman is different, it is not surprising that the change of life should affect every woman differently. The usual age for the menopause is some time late in the fourth decade of life. Some women have their change of life early in their forties; others have it in their early fifties, but the vast majority of them have it some time between the forty-fifth and fiftieth year.

The average woman has her menstrual function for about thirty or thirty-five years, dating from about the time or one year after the onset of her periods. In general the earlier that a woman starts her menstrual function the later she will stop. The converse is also true; those women who start their menstrual function late are apt to have an early change of life. Occasionally a family pattern is found but such patterns are neither striking nor reliable. It is worth mentioning at this time that any woman who continues to menstruate after her fiftieth year, should be particularly careful to have her yearly check-up or, in this instance, a check-up every six months. Cancer of the womb is more common in women who continue to menstruate beyond the fiftieth year.

Many women are quite disturbed when, approaching their late forties, they find irregular bleeding. They are disturbed because their friends tell them that irregular bleeding at this time simply means the change of life but information from the local cancer society (which is just beginning to filter down to many people after forty years), points out that irregular bleeding in the late forties may be a sign of serious disease. Actually there are no physical signs of menopause itself. There is no way on examination that the doctor can detect a change of life unless it has already occurred for some years, although the so-called screening smear, or cancer smear, not only tells us with astonishing accuracy if there is any sign of malignancy but also indicates if the patient is in the menopause. Most laboratories process these tests within three to seven days.

However, the important item in this change of life story has to do with the word "irregular." It is quite true that it is not at all uncommon for a woman to have irregular menstrual periods at or about the change of life. This means that a woman may skip periods. Irregular bleeding on the other hand is something entirely different. By irregular bleeding we mean vaginal bleeding—however much it may look like menstrual flow—which has no pattern. *Varying episodes of bleeding which may be of the proper length for a menstrual flow occurring as often as a week apart and as infrequently as five months apart represent irregular bleeding and must be investigated.* A woman who is skipping periods and is in her late forties is undoubtedly entering the menopause. A woman who has irregular bleeding is suspected of having uterine cancer until proven otherwise.

However, the pattern of bleeding is no criterium for the change of life either. Some women have the change of life by simply stopping their periods quite suddenly. They have what appears to be a perfectly normal menstrual flow on time and of the proper duration—and simply never have another one. Others skip periods as mentioned above, and still others have regular periods which become progressively scantier and scantier until they simply disappear.

The change of life affects women in other fashions as well. If you listen to very many women, they will tell you that a woman undergoing the change of life will always put on weight. The flippant answer to this is she certainly will—especially if she eats too much. There is no known mechanism by which a woman must necessarily put on weight simply because she has reached or is passing through the change of life. A change of life also has no appreciable effect on the sex drive of a woman, her sex appeal, or her sex appetite.

She can, however, be quite unhappy. Many women have no symptoms whatever at the time of their change of life, but those who do may be plagued by hot flashes and flushes. This refers to heat sensations associated with blushing of the skin of the chest, neck, and face, followed by a profuse sweating. These may occur day or night, perhaps more frequently at night, and can be precipitated by an emotional upset. Not infrequently they are associated with palpitation or pounding of the heart and the patient becomes frightened, agitated, and frustrated. When this happens, many women begin to think in terms of their friends who required psychiatric help at the time of their change of life.

It is true that some women require psychiatric assistance at the time of their change of life but usually this is because they have had some degree of mental illness all their lives and a mental crisis has been precipitated, so to speak, at the time of the change. For the woman whose mental health has always been in order, there is no reason to believe that she should become the victim of mental illness. On the other hand, symptoms as just described are so dramatic that they sometimes tend to focus the woman's attention on herself and her personal functions with the result that she becomes excessively aware of every ache, pain, twinge, and headache. Such a patient becomes confused and anxious and can only with great difficulty be relieved of her neurosis.

Medical assistance takes usually three forms:

1. It is imperative that a woman be made to understand what is happening to her and why. It is essential that she be reassured that, however dreadful her symptoms seem to be to her, there is an end in sight and she will eventually feel better.

2. The use of sedatives is the only thing that is required in most cases. A very small dose of phenobarbital to assuage anxiety is often sufficient to control the symptoms quite satisfactorily.

3. Substitute hormones may be prescribed when it is known that the patient's symptoms are due to the deficiency of hormones (through comparison to the time when she was functioning in full when her hormone levels were high). For many years physicians were wary of using hormones in any heavy dosage and for any prolonged period of time. Today they are still wary but they have learned that it is perfectly safe to employ hormones in small dosage (usually taken by mouth) provided there is no specific contraindication in the particular patient and provided the dosage is on a broken schedule, that is, say, twenty days out of each thirty. When employed in this fashion, the hormones not only offer the woman relief but, over a period from six to twelve months,

they can gradually be eliminated and the patient remains free of symptoms without the use of hormones.

The male may also have a change of life which is usually called the male climacteric. Not all men experience such a change, but if they do, the change is so gradual over a period of many years that they are unaware of it. Occasionally a man is encountered in whom the change of life occurs over a period of five years and his symptoms may be quite noticeable. From a physical point of view, the symptom is apt to be a gradually decreasing potency. He may have increasing difficulty in having an erection to complete the conjugal act of love with his wife. In an unusually sensitive man this may create real problems, but at least on a temporary basis they can be solved with the proper use of male hormones. More commonly the male climacteric is characterized by the development of anxiety and tension states, emotional irritability and lability, and even occasional episodes of irresponsibility. Sterility apart from impotence is not a specific characteristic of the male climacteric since there are many authentic records of men well beyond their sixties fathering children. Should the male experience a change of life, it generally occurs at age fifty or thereabouts, and it is treated by assurance, sedatives, and occasionally by hormones in much the same manner as the female.

The reaction to the change of life, of course, varies considerably. For some people, from this point on, life is down hill—but this is typical of people who think in terms of life being up and down. For others, whose habit it has always been to try for the home run ball all the time, this change, in male or female, is just another inning in the game of life.

Some people choose this time to try to prove to themselves and to everyone else that they are just as young as they ever were. Again, these are people who have been trying to prove things all their lives. Usually they turn out to be people who have always been reluctant to accept reality. Some of these unfortunate people get "burned" and even wander away from the marriage contract. But sturdy individuals who have always faced life and its problems have no more difficulty with the menopause than they do with their thirty-ninth birthday.

In the ensuing years after the menopause, and occasionally before it, the children begin to strike out on their own, form new careers, get married, develop families, and pursue their vocations in life. There comes a time when there are no children left in the home. In a child-centered society such as ours, the experts talk about the loneliness of the elderly couple. It is true that a consensus of opinion in this country indicates that the young married couple are better off (particularly starting their marriage) in their own home, however humble. Even this is not of critical importance usually; almost everyone wants to give the newly-weds an opportunity to make their own mistakes and to develop their own pattern of married life. It is true that the pace gets slower, *but not a few couples at this stage are not entirely unhappy at the slower pace.* The best insurance for a comfortable and continuing old age is to learn to pace oneself.

My experience indicates that parents like to keep in contact—preferably rather close contact—with their children, and they prize very highly the privilege of seeing their grandchildren grow in stature and intelligence. The happily married couple, however—no matter how many their years together—are content to remember and pleased to remind others that where two are in love, three's a crowd.

The biggest change, of course, is wrought by death. No one is ever totally prepared for the fact of the death of a partner, and when it occurs, it is always difficult to realize. A loss of a husband or wife always seems to carry with it a peculiar numbness that may take days or weeks, or even months, to erase. The family circle has been broken; the union of marriage now has a minus value. A bond so strong that no man could touch it has been torn asunder. It took the power of God to break it. This is a wrenching hurt that heals slowly. The power of Christian marriage, however, is such and its foundation so firmly laid, that the healing is assured because it is in the hands of the same One Who first sealed the bond. Fond memories are deep and personal, proud and strong and comforting. And faith in the certain knowledge of an ultimate reunion with Christ is what gives Christian marriage its purpose and its strength.

That is why the bereaved can stand at the grave of his beloved and murmur with the Church and friends and family "May the angels lead thee into paradise, may the martyrs re-receive thee at thy coming and take thee to Jerusalem the holy city. May the Choirs of angels receive thee and mayest thou with the once poor Lazarus have life everlasting." The bereaved partner in a Catholic marriage can say this because he carries with him a quiet conviction that when his day comes his beloved's voice from the vaults of heaven will join with the Church and family and friends to say the same.

There are changes in life, and they are many and varied and happy and sad. They reflect the frailty of human nature and the kindness of God. They can all be accepted and met within the framework of Christian marriage, for a Christian marriage is a union with God. And in God there is no change.

EPILOGUE

I have written from my experience with happily married people, and I have tried to capture the love and flavor and discipline that make Christian marriage the most romantic story in living. These happy people embrace a standard of morality and make themselves and their children aware of good and bad; they try to live the Christian message of love, making sacrifices willingly for their children or their life together; they are conscious and proud of progress wrought from the sometimes difficult task of living.

But the other side of the coin is also known to us. We are well aware of the national divorce rate—in our Pre-Cana Conferences we emphasize our conviction that happy marriages start with the proper partner. Broken marriages (and we all see them) prove a basic disinterest by too many people in marriage *as a contract* or in the value of a promise.

For some there seems to be something wrong with the good life: being moral is dull, having children is so prosaic;

to be fruitful or creative, some people apparently must be selfish; the development of the parent as an individual is more important than giving a child guidance, or time, or interest—or even life; the development of the child is so important that the parent is without authoritative status, and sometimes even honor, in his own home. Sacrifice no longer holds any pleasure; the satisfaction of a deed well done is an old cliché and the family circle has become so "square" that it must be broken or fled.

If the beginning of happiness is being content with what you have, then these people are doomed to unhappiness. The proper approach to Christian marriage pleads with you to be certain of what you have; to know it and grasp it—and leave the rest to God. When your partner in life is not only yours but is one whom you *know* to be yours and who is *glad* to be yours, then life is, indeed, worth living.

In Thornton Wilder's play *Our Town,* Emily is allowed to return to earth to relive her twelfth birthday. She is completely captivated and amazed by the picture of her family living the good life. She bursts out saying, "Oh earth, you're too wonderful for anybody to realize you. Do any human beings ever realize life while they have it? Every, every minute?"

Yes, Emily, yes. Some doctors see them every day.

QUESTIONS AND ANSWERS

At this point, I wish to consider a few questions which are commonly posed in premarital interviews and in Pre-Cana Conferences. Some of these questions do not fit quite properly into the previous chapters, others merit special attention because of their specific character.

1. **When may one spouse refuse the marital act to the other?** It is interesting that fifteen years ago this would have been considered in terms of when the woman might refuse the rights of marriage to her husband. It seems that women are losing the reticence which, in former times, they apparently felt was more ladylike and are now themselves asking often enough: When may the husband refuse the wife? Thus the general question as now posed is: for what reasons may one partner refuse the other partner the marital act? The answer is in cases of infidelity, mental or physical illness, severe injury, or physical exhaustion, or when one partner is alcoholic, drugged, or otherwise unreasonable.

2. **What is considered excessive vomiting in pregnancy?**
The technical name for this condition is *hyperemesis gravidarum*. It is a condition so striking that it has become known even by its Latin name. A significant percentage of pregnant women suffer nausea, although as previously indicated, many women do not. A relatively small percentage of women find the vomiting of pregnancy, for a regular period of two or three months, no more than annoying. Occasionally (that is to say, the average busy obstetrician may see one every five years) a pregnant woman vomits constantly. She cannot hold food or fluid in her stomach and sometimes vomits as frequently as every half hour. Eventually (and rather quickly) she becomes dehydrated and, therefore, must be hospitalized. In the hospital her fluids are replaced intravenously, mild sedatives are used, and large doses of vitamins are given intravenously. In this way the two most easily disturbed areas of nutrition (fluid balance and vitamins) are restored as quickly as possible. The woman is generally denied visitors —or visitors are kept at a very minimum—and often an effort is made to keep her alone in a darkened room. No solid food is given to her until her symptoms of nausea begin to disappear; then she is allowed foods cautiously and carefully and eventually sent home. Frequently these patients have several hospital admissions in the course of a pregnancy.

These women differ from most women who have nausea and vomiting in pregnancy not only in the severity of the vomiting and the physical difficulties that they encounter as a result of it but also because there are strong psychological reasons for these attacks. Most of these women have compelling fears or anxieties. If the issue which is bothering them can be discovered (and sometimes psychiatric help is required for this), and if they can be made to recognize the problem and helped to find their own solution to it, the excessive vomiting promptly stops.

3. **How often does the average couple have intercourse?**
The frequency of intercourse varies with the needs of the
couple, how recent the marriage is, the general health of the
partners, and the age of the partners. Newly married people
are generally young and very much in love; therefore, it is
not uncommon on the honeymoon for the couple to have
intercourse several times a day. This is not continued because,
as indicated elsewhere, the act of love is physically tiring.
Thus it is not unusual for a newly-wed couple at the end of a
month to have intercourse daily, or nearly daily. In some
cases, this continues for several months. By the end of a year,
the frequency of intercourse is usually two to three times a
week. Illness and fatigue influence frequency, of course, because of the physically exhausting character of the act. And
as a couple grows older, the effort required for the act will be
somewhat self-limiting. Also age naturally diminishes somewhat the frequency of sexual desire.

4. **What is the normal position for intercourse?** It is not
the purpose of a book of this type to go into detail on the
positions of intercourse. The positions for intercourse are
many and varied, and the final choice is a very personal subject. Usually the newly married couple try varying positions,
seeking to add variety and interest to their love-making. All
positions which involve the proper meeting of the genitals
in their properly performed act are normal. The most common position for intercourse is for the girl to recline and her
husband to face her. The most important aspect of position
is that the girl's legs be widely separated in order for intercourse to take place.

5. **Is a specialist really necessary at the delivery of a baby
or for the care of the baby afterwards?** The answers to these
questions will vary to some extent in different parts of the
country. In general, a specialist is not *necessary* in either instance. A competent family doctor generally takes care of

obstetrical cases which are normal and the common complaints of normal babies, including advice on growth and development. Actually, a competent family doctor, should he find some problem developing in the process of pregnancy or childbirth, usually is the first one to urge that expert knowledge be brought into the case. Similarly, if he finds something amiss with the baby, or if further advice is needed, a conscientious family doctor is always the first one to propose expert consultation. So we say again what we have said before: the most important aspect in the patient-physician relationship is the bond of faith that exists between them.

In some areas of the country of course, family doctors or general practitioners are well-nigh extinct. Patients have no choice but to seek a specialist. In other areas, family doctors or general practitioners will not take obstetrical or pediatric patients and obviously perforce the patient must seek specialist care.

6. **Can a woman become pregnant if she does not derive full satisfaction from intercourse?** Success in producing a pregnancy depends upon the couple's ability to perform the marriage act properly, so that the semen of the husband is deposited at the neck of the womb of the wife. It depends further on a clear passage existing for the semen to travel to meet the egg at the appropriate time. There is no relationship between pregnancy and orgasm, that is, the successful attainment of the full pleasure associated with the act of love.

7. **Can a woman get pregnant if her hymen is intact?** If a woman's hymen is intact usually it is not possible for the male organ to enter the vagina and for successful intercourse to take place. Nevertheless, it is possible for such a woman to get pregnant, although this is a rare occurrence. The answer lies in the fact that should the male deposit his sperm on the outside of his wife's vagina, on the lips of her front passage, in rare instances there is sufficient activity on the

part of the sperm to travel through the hymen, the length of the vagina, through the cervix, the uterus, and up into the tube to meet the egg. This act is known as vulvar coitus, that is, intercourse at the lips of the vagina. It does not represent properly performed marital relations. Any deliberate attempt to have vulvar coitus or intercourse at the lips of the vagina is unnatural and immoral and furthermore, a very unsatisfactory way of avoiding pregnancy.

8. **Does the fact that the woman's periods are irregular necessarily mean that she will have difficulty getting pregnant?** Not necessarily or even usually. There is relatively little correlation between the regularity or irregularity of a girl's menstrual cycle and her fertility. By irregular menstrual cycles, by the way, one usually means the girl's menstrual cycles vary more than ten days. The more important aspect of fertility is found in the answer to the question: "Is the girl ovulating (producing an egg) and regularly?" Irregularity of menstruation is much less important.

9. **Are there any rules or commonly given advice regarding the wedding night?** Tension for the bride generally begins about a month before the wedding date. During this period the average woman loses between seven to ten pounds, which adds to her worries (it adds at least the worry that maybe her wedding gown won't fit properly). In addition, the average bride, who has carefully selected her wedding date so that it does not coincide with her menstrual period, begins to wonder whether this is one of those carefully laid plans that will go awry. The bride becomes involved in a thousand and one details; most of the decisions are left to her and it seems everybody offers conflicting advice. The social pressures surrounding an American wedding are such that a woman often arrives at her wedding carrying a tremendous load of anxieties, worries, tensions, and fears—and yet manages somehow to walk down the aisle. It is not unusual,

therefore, for the bride to suffer a tremendous letdown immediately after the ceremony. A wise and gentle bridegroom, who should above all else be a considerate gentleman, will recognize this. This is when the bride learns (a) that in acquiring a husband, she has married a gentleman who also happens to be in love with her; (b) that being human, he is under some tension himself; and (c) that most women don't marry predatory males; (d) that her husband-lover will probably suggest that they postpone their love-making until the next morning when they both will be rested and eager.

10. **What is masturbation and is it serious?** Masturbation is the stimulation by the individual of his or her own genital organs to the point of complete sexual satisfaction. When properly understood and deliberately performed it is an unnatural and therefore immoral and sinful act. Masturbation of a type occurs in very small children. Among small children it comes as a direct result of the natural curiosity of the child who, in exploring his body, discovers an area, the genitals, which when touched and stimulated produces a pleasurable reaction (and in the boy an erection). An erection, of course, in itself does not necessarily have a sexual connotation since it can be induced accidentally—by rough clothing, for example, or even as a result of a dream.

Masturbation proper, as it is generally understood in family-doctor relationships, is most commonly found in the age group of 11 to 16 plus or minus a year. This is also called the age of puberty. Sexual stimulation to the point of orgasm occurs at least occasionally in both sexes. It sometimes represents a sporadic habit which has been carried over from the younger years as a result of the curiosity provocation. It is sometimes perpetuated by the "wet dreams" of a boy, which at least arouse his curiosity and sometimes disturb him. At such an age in a girl the irritation or at least the friction of the menstrual pad and the use of menstrual tampons, which occasionally accidentally stimulate the clitoris, serve to either renew masturbation or to provoke its continuance.

When this happens, the child has to be taught something about sex. Sex education in a rather complete form is a necessary basis to the proper solution of this problem. Proper sex education followed by self-discipline can serve to manage most of these problems. The child must be taught that he or she can and must exercise restraint. This is easier if children have been brought up in a family wherein the necessity for individual discipline for the good of the family has been demonstrated. The child must be taught that self-discipline is necessary for success in life in any phase of human endeavor. Self-discipline is the stuff, the stern stuff, of which ambition is made.

By the same token, it is well to bear in mind that the lack of self-discipline in any child can lead not only to masturbation but to homosexuality, alcoholism, or extramarital sexual relations. In the self-disciplined individual, these represent no problem.

With the possible exception of the introspective child, the one who is a little bit scrupulous, the one who finds it difficult to accept reassurance and whose personality won't allow him to forget any lapses he has made in his good intentions, masturbation is generally solved by a process of education *preferably coming from the parents* and assisted by further education and assurance by perhaps the family doctor and by a complete discussion with the confessor.

When masturbation is a confirmed habit in the adult, the individual may need (and usually does) the assistance of a competent psychiatrist and an experienced confessor.

11. **Is it true that the Church sometimes requires total abstinence from sexual relations in marriage?** No it is not true. However, the love of the couple for one another, the life of

one or both members of the partnership, the welfare of the children involved, or the integrity of the common life may require it. We have often commented in the course of this work that whosoever loves someone else asks the question, "What can I do *for* you?" Sometimes total abstinence is what the lover has to do for the beloved. To the very young, the immature, the selfish, or the inconsiderate this may seem like a hard life or an unusual demand to be made on the marriage contract. It is not an *easy* life, but there is nothing about the Christian life that was ever guaranteed to be easy. It *is* an unusual demand to be made on the marriage contract, but the contract *does* say for better, for worse, for richer, for poorer, in sickness and in health. The person genuinely in love does not consciously make a litany out of the contract. Rather his or her spontaneous act and reaction in the presence of some condition, usually medical, that might make the act of love itself dangerous will always be, "What can I do for you?"

12. Frequently at Pre-Cana meetings and at lectures on marriage we hear a British physician quoted who says that God will not be mocked; that is, so long as the Church approves of rhythm it is approving, in principle, of birth control —and a very poor form of birth control at that. Thus the Church is accused of intellectual dishonesty. Is the rhythm method "intellectual dishonesty"? There are a number of problems and points to be considered here. First, as indicated elsewhere in this work, rhythm under some circumstances cannot be used if the girl's menstrual cycle is totally irregular. Secondly, rhythm can be used provided the girl's cycle is within reasonable limits of regularity. Thus in many cases (some authorities place it as high as 70 per cent) with proper motivation, diligence, and a regular cycle, rhythm can be made to work successfully. The Church, therefore, is not being

intellectually dishonest in recommending rhythm since it has worked and can be made to work in a fairly high percentage of cases.

The real point at issue is the failure on the part of many people to understand the thinking behind the morality of rhythm. If we start with the premise that there exists a God, a First Cause, Who is the Creator of all heaven and earth, there must follow that all creation is dependent upon God. Man, being dependent upon God, has his own body, his faculties, and the world around him under his stewardship, for which he is accountable to God. Man finds in nature a divine plan.

One of the most important plans (obvious to man since his creation) has been the divine plan for the perpetuation of the human race. This is important because it deals with life itself. Life, human life, refers to body and soul. In our concept of life, man and wife in the sexual act cooperate with their Creator to produce new human life. The parents are privileged to offer the body of this child to God, who places a soul in it, creating new life. Thus, human life is brought into this world, and the human race is propagated by means of sexual intercourse.

Sexual intercourse is thus the part of the plan by which there is a union of the two components produced by the members of the partnership together with the creative act of God producing new life. If this is the natural plan of the generative process then man in his stewardship is obliged to maintain the integrity of this plan. Thus any means, condom, diaphragm, or jelly, which interferes with the normal relationship between the sexual act and the procreation which it intends is contrary to the plan of God and therefore is contrary to the very nature of the act itself. We are not concerned here whether the sperm or the egg may or may not merge as the result of intercourse. We are not concerned here with the fact that birth control as such prevents a possible pregnancy. What we are concerned with in the morality of contraception is that the use of positive contraceptive means interferes with the reproductive process, with the intention of the sexual act; it is a willful deviation of the natural processes following from the sexual act, an unnatural prevention of the proper order that follows from the naturally performed marital act. Thus the partners assume control over their own sexual functions whereas they have only a stewardship. This is probably epitomized in the term we hear today, used particularly by Dr. Allan Guttmacher, to the effect that man has a fifth freedom —a dominion over his procreative function. This we specifically deny. Man has a stewardship, a responsibility to use his reproductive function properly and according to the innate divine plan in the act itself, since the act in its proper fulfillment requires the specific cooperation of an act of God to produce new life.

This in no way implies that the secondary purposes of the marital act, including the normal pleasure to be derived from the act itself, should be denied to the couple or should be displaced from the position of importance which they rightly have. On the contrary, we maintain that in using rhythm— which simply means that the couple do not indulge in sexual relations at the time when the girl can become pregnant and that the couple may have the pleasure of the marital act itself at a time when they are reasonably certain the girl cannot conceive—a couple seeks some of the marital pleasures which the act of intercourse serves while they in no way interfere with the natural reproductive process of the act itself.

In rhythm, by not having intercourse at a time when pregnancy might take place (for a good and sufficient reason, which is always associated intimately with the welfare of the family and family living), the couple are abstaining; they are offering up the pleasure which would ordinarily be theirs in the marital act. They are induced to make a sacrifice for the sake of their love, if they have a good and sufficient reason and are capable of abstaining from the act of love during the time when the girl is fertile. Rhythm is a practice which is within the keeping of the divine plan of procreation.

In a sense the problem of the morality of rhythm tends to epitomize some of the differences in thinking between Roman Catholics and other Christians on the subject. Some of my non-Catholic friends are intrigued every year by the fact that, as they see it, "most of the Christian world" says "Peace on Earth Good Will to Men" whereas the Catholic says "Peace on Earth to Men of Good Will." In rhythm the Catholic recognizes his stewardship to God with regard to his own body, and in particular to his sexual function. By omitting the act at the time of possible pregnancy for the good of the family, he sacrifices all of the purposes of the act, all its pleasures, and all its responsibilities. His sacrifice in a sense is a measure of his good will.

FAMILY PRAYERS
and
READINGS FROM THE BIBLE

✠

A Prayer
to Be Said by Parents

IN BEHALF OF THEIR CHILDREN

¶ O Lord God, who hast called us to holy matrimony and
hast been pleased to render our union fruitful, thus making
glad the sublime state of life wherein Thou hast placed us,
by a certain likeness to Thine own infinite fruitfulness; we
heartily recommend to Thee our dear children; we entrust
them to Thy fatherly care and all-powerful protection, that
they may grow daily in Thy holy fear, may lead a perfect
Christian life and may be a source of consolation, not only
to us who have given them life, but also and chiefly to Thee,
who art their Creator.

¶ Behold, O Lord, in what a world they must pass their
lives; consider the cunning flatteries whereby the sons of
men everywhere endeavor to deprave their minds and hearts
with false doctrine and wicked example. Be watchful, O
Lord, to help and defend them; grant us the grace to be able
to guide them aright in the paths of virtue and in the way
of Thy commandments, by the righteous pattern of our own

life and practice, and our perfect observance of Thy holy law and that of our holy mother the Church; and in order that we may do so faithfully, make us certain of the grave danger that awaits us at the hands of Thy divine justice. Nevertheless all our efforts will be unavailing, unless Thou, O almighty and merciful God, shalt make them fruitful by Thy heavenly blessing.

¶ This Thy blessing, therefore, we humbly ask of Thee, from the bottom of our hearts, trusting in Thy great goodness and mercy hitherto shown unto us; we ask it for ourselves and for the children whom Thou hast been graciously pleased to give unto us. We dedicate them to Thee O Lord, do Thou keep them as the apple of Thine eye, and protect them under the shadow of Thy wings; do Thou make us worthy to come at last to heaven, together with them, giving thanks unto Thee, our Father, for the loving care Thou hast had of our entire family and praising Thee through endless ages.

AMEN.

(THE RACCOLTA: An indulgence of 300 days)

✠

𝔄 𝔓𝔯𝔞𝔶𝔢𝔯
𝔱𝔬 𝔅𝔢 𝔖𝔞𝔦𝔡 𝔟𝔶 ℭ𝔥𝔦𝔩𝔡𝔯𝔢𝔫

IN BEHALF OF THEIR PARENTS

¶ Almighty and everlasting God, who, in the secret counsels of Thine ineffable Providence, hast been pleased to call us into life by means of our parents, who thus partake of Thy divine power in our regard, mercifully hear the prayer of filial affection which we offer to Thee in behalf of those to whom Thou hast given a share of Thy fatherly mercy, in order that they might lavish upon us in our journey through life the consoling gift of Thy holy and generous love.

¶ Dear Lord, fill our parents with Thy choicest blessings; enrich their souls with Thy holy grace; grant that they may faithfully and constantly guard that likeness to Thy mystic marriage with Thy Church, which Thou didst imprint upon them on the day of their nuptials. Fill them with the spirit of holy fear, which is the beginning of wisdom, and continually move them to impart the same to their children; in such wise may they ever walk in the way of Thy commandments, and may their children be their joy in this earthly exile and their crown of glory in their home in heaven.

¶ Finally, Lord God, grant that both our father and our mother may attain to extreme old age and enjoy perpetual health in mind and body; may they deserve to sing Thy praises forever in our heavenly country in union with us, their children, giving Thee most hearty thanks that Thou hast bestowed upon them in this valley of tears the great gift of a share in the light of Thy infinite fruitfulness and of Thy divine fatherhood.

AMEN.

(THE RACCOLTA: An indulgence of 300 days)

A Prayer
to the Most Sacred Heart of Jesus

TO BE SAID BY MARRIED COUPLES (WITHOUT

CHILDREN) IN THEIR OWN BEHALF

¶ O Most Sacred Heart of Jesus, King and center of all hearts, dwell in our hearts and be our King: grant us by Thy grace to love each other truly and chastely, even as Thou hast loved Thine immaculate Bride, the Church, and didst deliver Thyself up for her.

¶ Bestow upon us the mutual love and Christian forbearance that are so acceptable in Thy sight, and a mutual patience in bearing each other's defects; for we are certain that no living creature is free from them. Permit not the slightest misunderstanding to mar that harmony of spirit which is the foundation of that mutual assistance in the many and varied hardships of life, to provide which woman was created and united inseparably to her husband.

¶ Grant, O Lord God, that between us there may be a constant and holy rivalry in our efforts to lead a truly Christian life, by virtue of which the divine image of Thy mystic union with Thy holy Church, which Thou didst deign to impress upon us on the happy day of our marriage, may shine forth more and more clearly; and so living may we, both of us, ascend into heaven and be found worthy to praise Thee and bless Thee forever.

AMEN.

(THE RACCOLTA: An indulgence of 300 days)

✠

A Prayer

to the Most Sacred Heart of Jesus

TO BE SAID BY MARRIED COUPLES (WITH

CHILDREN) IN THEIR OWN BEHALF

¶ O Most Sacred Heart of Jesus, King and center of all hearts, dwell in our hearts and be our King: grant us by Thy grace to love each other truly and chastely, even as Thou has loved Thine immaculate Bride, the Church, and didst deliver Thyself up for her.

¶ Bestow upon us the mutual love and Christian forbearance that are so acceptable in Thy sight, and a mutual patience in bearing each other's defects; for we are certain that no living creature is free from them. Permit not the slightest misunderstanding to mar that harmony of spirit which is the foundation of that mutual assistance in the many and varied hardships of life, to provide which woman was created and united inseparably to her husband.

¶ Grant, O Lord God, that between us there may be a constant and holy rivalry in striving to lead a perfect Christian life, by virtue of which the divine image of Thy mystic union with Holy Church, imprinted upon us on the happy day of our marriage, may shine forth more and more clearly. Grant, we beseech Thee, that our good example of Christian living may be a source of inspiration to our children to spur them on to conform their lives also to Thy holy Law; and finally, after this exile, may we be found worthy, by the help of Thy grace, for which we earnestly pray, to ascend into heaven, there to be joined with our children forever, and to praise and bless Thee through everlasting ages.

AMEN.

(THE RACCOLTA: An indulgence of 300 days)

Ecclesiasticus

xxv:1-32

With three things my spirit is pleased, which are approved before God and men:

The concord of brethren, and the love of neighbors, and man and wife that agree well together.

Three sorts my soul hateth, and I am greatly grieved at their life:

A poor man that is proud: a rich man that is a liar: an old man that is a fool, and doting.

The things that thou has not gathered in thy youth, how shalt thou find them in thy old age?

O how comely is judgment for a grey head, and for ancients to know counsel!

O how comely is wisdom for the aged and understanding and counsel to men of honour!

Much experience is the crown of old men, and the fear of God is their glory.

Nine things that are not to be imagined by the heart have I magnified, and the tenth I will utter to men with my tongue.

A man that hath joy of his children: and he that liveth and seeth the fall of his enemies.

Blessed is he that dwelleth with a wise woman, and that hath not slipped with his tongue, and that hath not served such as are unworthy of him.

Blessed is he that findeth a true friend, and that declareth justice to an ear that heareth.

How great is he that findeth wisdom and knowledge! but there is none above him that feareth the Lord.

The fear of God hath set itself above all things:

Blessed is the man, to whom it is given to have the fear of God: he that holdeth it, to whom shall he be likened?

The fear of God is the beginning of his love: and the beginning of faith is to be joined unto it.

The sadness of the heart is every plague: and the wickedness of a woman is all evil.

And a man will choose any plague, but the plague of the heart:

And any wickedness, but the wickedness of a woman:

And any affliction, but the affliction from them that hate him:

And any revenge, but the revenge of enemies.

There is no head worse than the head of a serpent:

And there is no anger above the anger of a woman. It will be more agreeable to abide with a lion and a dragon, than to dwell with a wicked woman.

The wickedness of a woman changeth her face: and she darkeneth her countenance as a bear: and sheweth it like sackcloth. In the midst of her neighbors,

Her husband groaned, and hearing he sighed a little.

All malice is short to the malice of a woman, let the lot of sinners fall upon her.

As the climbing of a sandy way is to the feet of the aged, so is a wife full of tongue to a quiet man.

Look not upon a woman's beauty, and desire not a woman for beauty.

A woman's anger and impudence and confusion is great.

A woman, if she have superiority, is contrary to her husband.

A wicked woman abateth the courage, and maketh a heavy countenance, and a wounded heart.

Feeble hands, and disjointed knees, a woman that doth not make her husband happy.

Proverbs

XXXI:10-31

Who shall find a valiant woman? far and from the uttermost coasts is the price of her.

The heart of her husband trusteth in her, and he shall have no need of spoils.

She will render him good, and not evil, all the days of her life.

She hath sought wool and flax, and hath wrought by the counsel of her hands.

She is like the merchant's ship, she bringeth her bread from afar.

And she hath risen in the night, and given a prey to her household, and victuals to her maidens.

She hath considered a field, and bought it: with the fruit of her hands she hath planted a vineyard.

She hath girded her loins with strength, and hath strengthened her arm.

She hath tasted and seen that her traffic is good: her lamp shall not be put out in the night.

She hath put out her hand to strong things, and her fingers have taken hold of the spindle.

She hath opened her hand to the needy, and stretched out her hands to the poor.

She shall not fear for her house in the cold of snow: for all her domestics are clothed with double garments.

She hath made for herself clothing of tapestry: fine linen, and purple is her covering.

Her husband is honorable in the gates, when he sitteth among the senators of the land.

She made fine linen, and sold it, and delivered a girdle to the Chanaanite.

Strength and beauty are her clothing and she shall laugh in the latter day.

She hath opened her mouth to wisdom, and the law of clemency is on her tongue.

She hath looked well to the paths of her house, and hath not eaten her bread idle.

Her children rose up, and called her blessed: her husband, and he praised her.

Many daughters have gathered together riches: thou hast surpassed them all.

Favor is deceitful, and beauty is vain: the woman that feareth the Lord, she shall be praised.

Give her of the fruit of her hands: and let her works praise her in the gates.

Ecclesiasticus

XXVI: 1-4, 16-24

Happy is the husband of a good wife: for the number of his years is double.

A virtuous woman rejoiceth her husband, and shall fulfil the years of his life in peace.

A good wife is a good portion, she shall be given in the portion of them that fear God, to a man for his good deeds.

Rich or poor, if his heart is good, his countenance shall be cheerful at all times.

The grace of a diligent woman shall delight her husband, and shall fat his bones.

Her discipline is the gift of God.

Such is a wise and silent woman, and there is nothing so much worth as a well instructed soul.

A holy and shamefaced woman is grace upon grace.

And no price is worthy of a continent soul.

As the sun when it riseth to the world in the high places of God, so is the beauty of a good wife for the ornament of her house.

As the lamp shining upon the holy candlestick, so is the beauty of the face in a ripe age.

As golden pillars upon bases of silver, so are the firm feet upon the soles of a steady woman.

As everlasting foundations upon a solid rock, so the commandments of God in the heart of a holy woman.

Ecclesiasticus

XXIII:24-38

To a man that is a fornicator all bread is sweet, he will not be weary of sinning unto the end.

Every man that passeth beyond his own bed, despising his own soul, and saying: Who seeth me?

Darkness compasseth me about, and the walls cover me, and no man seeth me: whom do I fear? the most High will not remember my sins.

And he understandeth not that his eye seeth all things, for such a man's fear driveth from him the fear of God, and the eyes of men fearing him:

And he knoweth not that the eyes of the Lord are far brighter than the sun, beholding round about all the ways of men, and the bottom of the deep, and looking into the hearts of men, into the most hidden parts.

For all things were known to the Lord God, before they were created: so also after they were perfected he beholdeth all things.

This man shall be punished in the streets of the city, and he shall be chased as a colt: and where he suspected not, he shall be taken.

And he shall be in disgrace with all men, because he understood not the fear of the Lord.

So every woman also that leaveth her husband, and bringeth in an heir by another:

For first she hath been unfaithful to the law of the most High: and secondly, she hath offended against her husband: thirdly she hath fornicated in adultery, and hath gotten her children of another man.

This woman shall be brought into the assembly, and inquisition shall be made of her children.

Her children shall not take root, and her branches shall bring forth no fruit.

She shall leave her memory to be cursed, and her infamy shall not be blotted out.

And they that remain shall know, that there is nothing better than the fear of God: and that there is nothing sweeter than to have regard to the commandments of the Lord.

It is great glory to follow the Lord: for length of days shall be received from him.

Wisdom

XIII:1-5

But all men are vain, in whom there is not the knowledge of God: and who by these good things that are seen, could not understand him that is, neither by attending to the works have acknowledged who was the workman:

But have imagined either the fire, or the wind, or the swift air, or the circle of the stars, or the great water, or the sun and the moon, to be the gods that rule the world.

With whose beauty, if they, being delighted, took them to be gods: let them know how much the Lord of them is more beautiful than they: for the first author of beauty made all those things.

Or if they admired their power and their effects, let them understand by them, that he that made them, is mightier than they:

For by the greatness of the beauty, and of the creature, the creator of them may be seen, so as to be known thereby.

Psalms

LXXXIX

Lord, thou has been our refuge from generation to generation.

Before the mountains were made, or the earth and the world was formed; from eternity and to eternity thou art God.

Turn not man away to be brought low: and thou hast said: Be converted, O ye sons of men.

For a thousand years in thy sight are as yesterday, which is past.

And as a watch in the night, things that are counted nothing, shall their years be.

In the morning man shall grow up like grass; in the morning he shall flourish and pass away: in the evening he shall fall, grow dry, and wither.

For in thy wrath we have fainted away: and are troubled in thy indignation.

Thou hast set our iniquities before thy eyes: our life in the light of thy countenance.

For all our days are spent; and in thy wrath we have fainted away.

Our years shall be considered as a spider: the days of our years in them are three-score and ten years.

But if in the wrong they are fourscore years: and what is more of them is labor and sorrow.

For mildness is come upon us: and we shall be corrected.

Who knoweth the power of thy anger, and for thy fear can number thy wrath?

So make thy right hand known: and men learned in heart, in wisdom.

Return, O Lord, how long? and be entreated in favor of thy servants.

We are filled in the morning with thy mercy: and we have rejoiced, and are delighted all our days.

We have rejoiced for the days in which thou hast humbled us: for the years in which we have seen evils.

Look upon thy servants and upon their works: and direct their children.

And let the brightness of the Lord our God be upon us: and direct thou the works of our hands over us; yea, the work of our hands do thou direct.

A Betrothal Rite

The priest (vested in surplice and white stole) with his assistants (vested in surplice) awaits the couple at the communion table. At hand are the holy water stoup and the altar missal. As the man and woman come forward with the two witnesses they have chosen, the following antiphon and psalm are spoken or sung on the eighth psalm tone:

ANTIPHON: To the Lord I will tender my promise: in the presence of all His people.

Psalm 126

Unless the house be of the Lord's building, in vain do the builders labor.

Unless the Lord be the guard of the city, 'tis in vain the guard keeps sentry.

It is futile for you to rise before daybreak, to be astir in the midst of darkness,

Ye that eat the bread of hard labor; for He deals bountifully to His beloved while they are sleeping.

Behold, offspring result from God's giving, a fruitful womb won the regard of His blessing.

Like arrows in the hand of the warrior, are children begotten of a youthful father.

Happy the man who has filled therewith his quiver; they shall uphold him in contending at the gate with his rival.

Glory be to the Father and to the Son, and to the Holy Spirit.

As it was in the beginning, is now, and forever, through endless ages. Amen.

ANTIPHON: To the Lord I will tender my promise: in the presence of all his people.

The priest now addresses them:

Allocution

Beloved of Christ: It is in the dispensation of Divine Providence that you are called to the holy vocation of marriage. For this reason you present yourselves today before Christ and His Church, before His sacred minister and the devout people of God, to ratify in solemn manner the engagement bespoken between you. At the same time you entreat the blessing of the Church upon your proposal, as well as the earnest supplications of the faithful here present, since you fully realize that what has been inspired and guided by the will of your heavenly Father requires equally His grace to be brought to a happy fulfillment.

We are confident that you have given serious and prayerful deliberation to your pledge of wedlock; moreover, that you have sought counsel from the superiors whom God has placed over you. In the time that intervenes, you will prepare for the sacrament of matrimony by a period of virtuous courtship, so that when the happy and blessed day arrives for you to give yourselves irrevocably to each other, you will have laid a sound spiritual foundation for long years of godly prosperity on earth and eventual blessedness together in the life to come. May the union you propose one day to consummate as man and wife be found worthy to be in all truth a sacramental image and reality of the union of Christ and His beloved Bride, the Church. This grant, Thou Who livest and reignest, God, forever and evermore.

Ry.: Amen.

The priest now bids the couple join their right hands, while they repeat after him the following:

THE MAN: In the name of Our Lord, I, *N.N.*, promise that I will one day take thee, *N.N.*, as my wife, according to the ordinances of God and Holy Church. I will love thee even as myself. I will keep faith and loyalty to thee, and so in thy necessities aid and comfort thee; which things and all that a man ought to do unto his espoused I promise to do unto thee and to keep by the faith that is in me.

THE WOMAN: In the name of Our Lord, I, *N.N.*, in the form and manner wherein thou hast promised thyself unto me, do declare and affirm that I will one day bind and oblige myself unto thee, and will take thee, *N.N.*, as my husband. And all that thou hast pledged unto me I promise to do and keep unto thee, by the faith, that is in me.

Then the priest takes the two ends of his stole and in the form of a cross places them over the clasped hands of the couple. Holding the stole in place with his left hand, he says:

PRIEST: I bear witness of your solemn proposal and I declare you betrothed. In the name of the Father, and of the Son, and of the Holy Spirit.

℞.: Amen.

As he pronounces the last words, he sprinkles them with holy water in the form of a cross.

Thereupon he blesses the engagement ring:

℣.: Our help is in the name of the Lord,

℞.: Who made heaven and earth.

℣.: O Lord, hear my prayer.

℞.: And let my cry come unto Thee.

℣.: The Lord be with you.

℞.: And with thy spirit. Let us pray.

O God Almighty, Creator and preserver of the human race, and the giver of everlasting salvation, deign to allow the Holy Spirit, the Consoler to come with His blessing upon this ring. Through Our Lord, Jesus Christ, Thy Son, Who liveth and reigneth with Thee in the unity of the Holy Spirit, God, for endless ages.

℞.: Amen.

The ring is sprinkled with holy water.

℣.: *Adjutorium nostrum in nomine Domini*

℞.: *Qui fecit caelum et terram.*

℣.: *Domine, exaudi orationem meam.*

℞.: *Et clamor meus ad te veniat.*

℣.: *Dominus vobiscum.*

℞.: *Et cum spiritu tuo. Oremus*

Omnipotens Deus, Creator et conservator humani generis, ac largitor aeternae salutis, permitte digneris Spiritum Sanctum Paraclitum super hunc annulum. Per Dominum Nostrum Jesum Christum, Filium Tuum, Qui Tecum vivit et regnat in unitate Spiritus Sancti, Deus, per omnia saecula saeculorum.

℞.: *Amen.*

Et aspergatur aqua benedicta.

The man takes the ring and places it first on the index finger of the left hand of the woman, saying, "In the name of the Father," then on the middle finger, adding, "and of the Son"; finally placing and leaving it on the ring finger, he concludes, "and of the Holy Spirit."

The priest opens the missal at the beginning of the Canon, and presents the page imprinted with the crucifixion to be kissed first by the man and then by the woman.

If Mass does not follow (or even if Mass is to follow, if he deems it opportune), the priest may read the following passages from Sacred Scripture:

Tobias 7:8

Tobias said: I will not eat nor drink here this day, unless thou first grant me my petition, and promise to give me Sara thy daughter. . . . The angel said to Raguel: Be not afraid to give her to this man, for to him who feareth God is thy daughter due to be his wife; therefore another could not have her. . . . And Raguel taking the right hand of his daughter, he gave it unto the right hand of Tobias, saying: The God of Abraham, and the God of Isaac, and the God of Jacob be with you, and may He join you together, and fulfill His blessing in you. And taking paper they made a writing of the marriage. And afterwards they made merry, blessing God. . . . Then Tobias exhorted the virgin, and said to her: Sara, arise, and let us pray to God today, and tomorrow, and the next day; because for these three nights we are joined to God; and when the third night is over, we will be in our own wedlock. For we are the children of saints, and we must not be joined together like heathens that know not God. So they both arose, and prayed earnestly both together that health might be given them.

℟.: Thanks be to God.

John 15:4-12

At that time, Jesus said to His disciples: Abide in Me, and I in you. As the branch cannot bear fruit of itself, unless it abide in the vine, so neither can you, unless you abide in Me. I am the vine; you the branches. He that abideth in Me, and I in him, the same beareth much fruit; for without Me you can do nothing. If any one does not abide in Me, he shall be cast forth as a branch, and shall wither, and they shall gather him up, and cast him into the fire, and he burneth. If you abide in Me, and my words abide in you, you shall ask whatever you will, and it shall be done unto you. In this is my Father glorified; that you bring forth very much fruit, and become my disciples. As the Father hath loved Me, I also have loved you. Abide in My love. If you keep My commandments, you shall abide in My love; as I also have kept my Father's commandments, and do abide in His love. These things I have spoken to you, that My joy may be in you, and your joy may be filled. This is My commandment, that you love one another, as I have loved you.

℟.: Praise be to thee, O Christ!

Lastly, the priest extends his hands over the heads of the couple and says:

May God bless your bodies and your souls. May he shed His blessing upon you as He blessed Abraham, Isaac, and Jacob. May the hand of the Lord be upon you, may He send His holy Angel to guard you all the days of your life. Amen. Go in peace!

Before leaving the church, the betrothed couple as well as the witnesses will affix their signatures to the document previously prepared for this purpose.

✠

Marriage Service and Mass

THE RITUAL FOR THE CELEBRATION

OF MATRIMONY

The priest, vested in surplice and white stole (or, if the Nuptial Mass is to follow, vested as for Mass, yet without the maniple), in the hearing of the chosen witnesses, asks the man and the woman separately as follows, concerning their consent. First he asks the bridegroom, who should stand at the right hand of the bride:

N., wilt thou take N., here present, for thy lawful wife, according to the rite of our holy Mother the Church?
℟.: I will.

Then the priest asks the bride:

N., wilt thou take N., here present, for thy lawful husband, according to the rite of our holy Mother the Church?
℟.: I will.

Having obtained their mutual consent, the priest bids the man and the woman join their right hands. Then they pledge themselves each to the other as follows, repeating the words after the priest.

The man first says:

I, N.N., take thee, N.N., for my lawful wife, to have and to hold, from this day forward, for better, for worse, for richer, for poorer, in sickness and in health, until death do us part.

Then the woman says:

I, N.N., take thee, N.N., for my lawful husband, to have and to hold, from this day forward, for better, for worse, for richer, for poorer, in sickness and in health, until death do us part.

The priest then says:

I join you together in marriage, in the name of the Father, ✠ and of the Son, and of the Holy Ghost. Amen.

Ego conjungo vos in matrimonium, in nomine Patris, ✠ et Filii, et Spiritus Sancti.   Amen.

He then sprinkles them with holy water. This done, he blesses the ring, saying:

Our help is in the name of the Lord.

Adjutorium nostrum in nomine Domini.

℟.: Who hath made heaven and earth.

℟.: Qui fecit caelum et terram.

℣.: O Lord, hear my prayer.

℣.: Domine, exaudi orationem meam.

℟.: And let my cry come un- to Thee.

℣.: The Lord be with you.

℟.: And with thy spirit.

Let us pray

Bless, ✠ O Lord, this ring, which we bless ✠ in Thy name, that she who shall wear it, keeping true faith unto her spouse, may abide in Thy peace and in obedi- ence to Thy will, and ever live in mutual love. Through Christ, our Lord. ℟. Amen.

℟.: Et clamor meus ad Te veniat.

℣.: Dominus vobiscum.

℟.: Et cum spiritu tuo.

Oremus

Benedic, ✠ Domine, an- nulum hunc, quem nos in Tuo nomine benedicimus, ✠ ut quae eum gestaverit, fidelitatem in- tegram suo sponso tenens, in pace et voluntate Tua perma- neat, atque in mutua charitate semper vivat. Per Christum Dominum nostrum. ℟. Amen.

Then the priest sprinkles the ring with holy water in the form of a cross; and the bridegroom having received the ring from the hand of the priest places it on the third finger of the left hand of the bride, saying:

With this ring I thee wed and I plight unto thee my troth.

Then the priest says:

In the name of the Father, ✠ and of the Son, and of the Holy Ghost. Amen.

In nomine Patris, ✠ et Filii, et Spiritus Sancti. Amen.

This done, the priest adds:

℣.: Confirm, O God, that which Thou hast wrought in us.

℟.: From Thy holy temple, which is in Jerusalem.

℣.: Lord, have mercy.

℟.: Christ, have mercy.

℣.: Confirma hoc, Deus, quod operatus es in nobis.

℟.: A templo sancto Tuo quod est in Jerusalem.

℣.: Kyrie eleison.

℟.: Christe eleison.

℣.: Lord, have mercy.

Our Father, etc.

℣.: And lead us not into temptation.

℞.: But deliver us from evil.

℣.: Save Thy servants.

℞.: Who hope in Thee, O my God.

℣.: Send them help, O Lord, from Thy holy place.

℞.: And defend them out of Sion.

℣.: Be unto them, Lord, a tower of strength.

℞.: From the face of the enemy.

℣.: O Lord, hear my prayer.

℞.: And let my cry come unto Thee.

℣.: The Lord be with you.

℞.: And with thy spirit.

Let us pray.

℣.: Kyrie eleison.

Pater noster (secreto).

℣.: Et ne nos inducas in tentationem.

℞.: Sed libera nos a malo.

℣.: Salvos fac servos Tuos.

℞.: Deus meus, sperantes in Te.

℣.: Mitte eis, Domine, auxilium de sancto.

℞.: Et de Sion tuere eos.

℣.: Esto eis, Domine, turris fortitudinis.

℞.: A facie inimici.

℣.: Domine, exaudi orationem meam.

℞.: Et clamor meus ad Te veniat.

℣.: Dominus vobiscum.

℞.: Et cum spiritu tuo.

Oremus

Look down with favor, O Lord, we beseech Thee, upon these Thy servants, and graciously protect this Thine ordinance, whereby Thou hast provided for the propagation of mankind; that they who are joined together by Thy authority may be preserved by Thy help; through Christ our Lord. Amen.

Respice, quaesumus, Domine, super hos famulos Tuos, et institutis Tuis, quibus propagationem humani generis ordinasti, benignus assiste, ut qui Te auctore junguntur, Te auxiliante serventur. Per Christum Dominum nostrum.

Amen.

Then, if the Nuptial Blessing is to be given, follows the

✠

Mass for the Bridegroom and Bride

Deus Israel

The Beginning of Mass then:

Introit. Tob. 7, 15; 8, 17

May the God of Israel join you together; and may He be with you, Who was merciful to two only children; and now, O Lord, make them bless Thee more fully. *Ps. 127, 1.* Blessed are all they that fear the Lord; that walk in His ways. ℣. Glory.

Deus, Israel, conjugat vos; et ipse sit vobiscum, qui misertus est duobus unicis; et nunc, Domine, fac eos plenius benedicere te. [PS. 127, 1] *Beati omens qui timent Dominum: qui ambulant in viis ejus.* ℣. *Gloria Patri.*

337

KYRIE; GLORIA, then:

Prayer

Graciously hear us, almighty and merciful God, that what is accomplished by our ministry may be perfected by Thy blessing. Through our Lord.

Exaudi nos, omnipotens et misericors Deus: ut, quod nostro ministratur officio, tua benedictione potius impleatur. Per Dominum.

Epistle. Eph. 5, 22-23

Lesson from the Epistle of blessed Paul the Apostle to the Ephesians.

Lectio Epistolae beati Pauli Apostoli ad Ephesios.

Brethren: Let wives be subject to their husbands as to the Lord: because a husband is head of the wife, just as Christ is head of the Church, being Himself Saviour of the body. But just as the Church is subject to Christ, so also let wives be to their husbands in all things. Husbands, love your wives, just as Christ also loved the Church, and delivered himself up for her, that He might sanctify her, cleansing her in the bath of water by means of the word; in order that He might present to Himself the Church in all her glory,

Fratres: Mulieres viris suis subditae sint, sicut Domino: quoniam vir caput est mulieris: sicut Christus caput est Ecclesiae: Ipse, salvator, corporis ejus: Sed sicut Ecclesia subjecta est Christo, ita et mulieres viris suis in omnibus. Viri, diligite uxores vestras, sicut et Christus dilexit Ecclesiam, et seipsum tradidit pro ea, ut illam sanctificaret, mundans lavacro aquae in verbo vitae, ut exhiberet ipse sibi gloriosam Ecclesiam, non habentem maculam, aut rugam, aut aliquid hujusmodi, sed ut sit sancta et immaculata. Ita et viri debent diligere uxores suas, ut corpora sua. Qui suam ux-

not having spot or wrinkle or any such thing, but that she might be holy and without blemish. Even thus ought husbands also to love their wives as their own bodies. He who loves his own wife, loves himself. For no one ever hated his own flesh; on the contrary he nourishes and cherishes it, as Christ also does the Church (because we are members of His body, made from His flesh and from His bones). "For this cause a man shall leave his father and mother, and cleave to his wife; and the two shall become one flesh." This is a great mystery—I mean in reference to Christ and to the Church. However, let each one of you also love his wife just as he loves himself; and let the wife respect her husband.

orem diligit, seipsum diligit. Nemo enim unquam carnem suam odio habuit: sed nutrit, et fovet eam, sicut et Christus Ecclesiam: quia membra sumus corporis ejus, de carne ejus, et de ossibus ejus. Propter hoc relinquet homo patrem et matrem suam, et adhaerebit uxori suae: et erunt duo in carne una. Sacramentum hoc magnum est, ego autem dico in Christo, et in Ecclesia. Verumtamen et vos singuli, unusquisque uxorem suam, sicut seipsum diligat: uxor autem timeat virum suum.

From Septuagesima to Easter the Lesser Alleluia is replaced by the Tract, in Paschal-time the Gradual and Tract are replaced by the Greater Alleluia.

Gradual.   Ps. 127, 3

Thy wife shall be as a fruitful vine on the sides of thy house. ℣. Thy children as oliveplants round about thy table.

Uxor tua sicut vitis abundans in lateribus domus tuae. ℣. Filii tui sicut novellae olivarum in circuitu mensae tuae.

Lesser Alleluia

Alleluia, alleluia. ℣. *Ps. 19, 3.* May the Lord send you help from the sanctuary, and defend you out of Sion. Alleluia.

Alleluja, alleluja. ℣. [ps. 19. 3.] Mittat vobis Dominus auxilium de sancto: et de Sion tueatur Vos. Alleluja.

Tract.   Ps. 127, 4-6

Behold, thus shall the man be blessed that feareth the Lord. ℣. May the Lord bless thee out of Sion; and mayest thou see the good things of Jerusalem all the days of thy life. ℣. And mayest thou see thy children's children: peace upon Israel.

Ecce sic benedicetur omnis homo, qui timet Dominum. ℣. benedicat tibi Dominus ex Sion: et videas bona Jerusalem omnibus diebus vitae tuae. ℣. Et videas filios filiorum tuorum: pax super Israel.

Greater Alleluia

Alleluia, alleluia. ℣. *Ps. 19, 3.* May the Lord send you help from the sanctuary and defend you out of Sion, alleluia. ℣. *Ps. 133, 3.* May the Lord out of Sion bless you; He that made heaven and earth. Alleluia.

Alleluja, alleluja. ℣. [ps. 19, 3.] Mittat vobis Dominus auxilium de Sancto: et de Sion tueatur vos. Alleluja. ℣. [ps. 133, 3.] Benedicat vobis Dominus ex Sion: qui fecit caelum et terram. Alleluja.

MUNDA COR MEUM, then:

Gospel.   Matt. 19, 3-6

✠ Continuation of the holy Gospel according to St. Matthew.

At that time, there came to Jesus some Pharisees, testing Him, and saying: "Is it lawful for a man to put away his wife for any cause?" But He answered and said to them: "Have you not read that the Creator, from the beginning, made them male and female, and said, 'For this cause a man shall leave his father and mother, and cleave to his wife, and the two shall become one flesh'? Therefore, now they are no longer two, but one flesh. What therefore God has joined together, let no man put asunder."

✠ *Sequentia sancti Evangelii secundum Matthaeum.*

In illo tempore: Accesserunt ad Jesum pharisaei tentantes eum, et dicentes: Si licet homini dimittere uxorem suam quacumque ex causa? Qui respondens, ait eis: Non legistis, quia qui fecit hominem ab initio, masculum et feminam fecit eos? et dixit: Propter hoc dimittet homo patrem, et matrem, et adhaerebit uxori suae, et erunt duo in carne una. Itaque jam non sunt duo, sed una caro. Quod ergo Deus conjunxit, homo non separet.

Offertory.   Ps. 30, 15, 16

In Thee, O Lord, have I put my trust; I said, Thou art my God; my times are in Thy hands.

In te speravi Domine: dixi: tu es Deus meus: in manibus tuis tempora mea.

OFFERTORY PRAYERS, then:

Secret

Receive, we beseech Thee, O Lord, the offering which we make to Thee on behalf of the sacred bond of wedlock, and be Thou the disposer of the work of which Thou art the author. Through our Lord.

Suscipe, quaesumus, Domine, pro sacra connubii lege munus oblatum: et, cujus largitor es operis, esto dispositor. Per Dominum.

After the Pater Noster, *the priest, before continuing the Mass, proceeds one step to the Epistle side of the altar, and turning toward the bridegroom and bride, who are kneeling at the altar steps, says over them the following prayers.*

Prayer

Mercifully hear our prayers, O Lord, and graciously protect Thine ordinance, whereby Thou hast provided for the propagation of mankind, that this union made by Thy authority may be preserved by Thy help. Through our Lord.

Propitiare, Domine, supplicationibus nostris, et institutis tuis, quibus propagationem humani generis ordinasti, benignus assiste: ut, quod te auctore jungitur, te auxiliante servetur. Per Dominum.

Prayer

O God, Who by Thy mighty power hast made all things out of nothing; Who, in the beginning having set

Deus, qui potestate virtutis tuae de nihilo cuncta fecisti: qui dispositis universitatis exordiis, homini ad imaginem Dei fecto,

up the world, didst bestow on man, whom Thou hadst created in Thine own likeness, the inseparable help of woman, fashioning her body from his very flesh, and thereby teaching us that it is never lawful to put asunder what it has pleased Thee to make of one substance; O God, Who hast consecrated wedlock by a surpassing mystery, since in the marriage-bond Thou didst foreshow the union of Christ with the Church; O God, by Whom woman is joined to man, and that alliance which Thou didst ordain from the beginning is endowed with a blessing, which alone was not taken away, either in punishment of original sin or by the sentence of the flood, look down in mercy upon this Thy handmaid who, being about to enter upon wedded life, seeks to be strengthened by Thy protection; may the yoke she has to bear be one of love and peace; true and chaste may she marry in Christ, and be a follower of holy women; may she be pleasing to her husband like Rachel; prudent like Rebecca; long-lived and faith-

ideo inseparabile mulieris adjutorium condidisti, ut femineo corpori de virili dares carne principium, docens quod ex uno placuisset, institui, nunquam licere disjungi: Deus, qui tam excellenti mysterio conjugalem copulam consecrasti, ut Christi et Ecclesiae sacramentum praesignares in faedere nuptiarum: Deus, per quem mulier jungitur viro, et societas principaliter ordinata, ea benedictione donatur, quae sola nec per originalis peccati paenam, nec per diluvii est ablata sententiam: respice propitius super hanc famulam tuam, quae maritali jungenda consortio, tua se expetit protectione muniri: sit in ea jugum dilectionis, et pacis: fidelis et casta nubat in Christo, imitatrixque sanctarum permaneat feminarum: sit amabilis viro suo, ut Rachel: sapiens, ut Rebecca: longaeva et fidelis, ut Sara: nihil in ea ex actibus suis ille auctor praevaricationis usurpet: nexa fidei, mandatisque permaneat: uni thoro juncta, contactus illicitos fugiat: muniat infirmitatem suam robore disciplinae: sit verecundia gravis, pudore venerabilis, doctrinis caelestibus erudita: sit fecunda in sobole, sit probata et innocens: et ad beatorum requiem,

ful like Sara; may the author of sin have no share in any of her actions; may she remain firmly attached to the faith and the commandments, and being joined to one man in wedlock, may she fly all unlawful addresses; may she fortify her weakness by strong discipline; may she be respected for her seriousness and venerated for her modesty; may she be well versed in heavenly lore; may she be fruitful in offspring. May her life be pure and blameless; and may she attain to the rest of the blessed in the kingdom of heaven. May they both see their children's children even to the third and fourth generation and arrive at a happy old age; through Our Lord Jesus Christ Thy Son, Who liveth and reigneth with Thee in the unity of the Holy Ghost, one God world without end. Amen.

atque adcaelestia regna perveniat: et videant ambo filios filiorum suorum, usque in tertiam et quartem generationem, et ad optatam perveniant senectutem. Per eumdem Dominum. Amen.

The priest then continues the Mass, saying the prayer Libera, as in the Canon, and the bridegroom and bride ought to receive Holy Communion at the time appointed therefor.

PREFACE FOR WEEKDAYS, then:

Communion. Ps. 127, 4, 6

Behold, thus shall every man be blessed that feareth the Lord: and mayest thou see thy children's children: peace be upon Israel.

Ecce sic benedicetur omnis homo, qui timet Dominum: et videas filios filiorum tuorum: pax super Israel.

Postcommunion

We beseech Thee, almighty God, in Thy great goodness, to show favor to that order of things which Thou Thyself hast established, and to keep in abiding peace those whom Thou hast joined together in lawful union. Through our Lord.

Quaesumus omnipotent Deus, instituta providentiae tuae pio favore comitare: ut, quos legitime societate connectis, longaeva pace custodias. Per Dominum.

Before blessing the people, the priest again turns to the bridegroom and bride, and blesses them in particular saying:

May the God of Abraham, the God of Isaac, and the God of Jacob, be with you, and may He fullfil His blessing in you: that you may see your children's children even to the third and fourth generation, and may afterwards have life everlasting, by the grace of Our Lord Jesus

Deus Abraham, Deus Isaac, et Deus Jacob sit vobiscum: et ipse adimpleat benedictionem suam in vobis: ut videatis filios filiorum vestrorum usque ad tertiam et quartam generationem, et postea vitam aeternam habeatis sine fine: adjuvante Domino nostro Jesu Christo, qui cum Patre et Spiritu

Christ, Who, with the Father and the Holy Ghost, liveth and reigneth God, world without end. ℟. Amen.

sancto vivit et regnat Deus, per omnia saecula saeculorum. ℟. *Amen.*

Lastly he sprinkles them with holy water and admonishes both on the responsibilities of the married state.

CONCLUDING PRAYERS.

BIBLIOGRAPHY

Bible. Douay Version. New York: P. J. Kenedy & Sons, 1963.

Bonzelet, Honoratus. *Mixed Marriages and Prenuptial Instructions.* Milwaukee: Bruce Publishing Company, 1942.

Christopher, Joseph (ed.). *Raccolta.* Rev. Ed. New York: Benziger, 1963.

Conway, Bertrand L. *The Question Box.* pap. New York: All Saints Press, 1963.

Conway, James D. *What They Ask About Marriage.* pap. Notre Dame: Fides Publishers, Inc., 1955.

Haussamen, Florence and Mary Guitar. *The Divorce Handbook.* New York: G. P. Putnam's Sons, 1960.

Kelly, Philip C. *The Catholic Book of Marriage.* New York: Farrar, Straus & Company, 1951.

Lord, Daniel A. *Some Notes for . . . The Guidance of Parents.* St. Louis: Queen's Work, 1944.

McManus, William F. *Marriage Guide for Engaged Catholics.* pap. New York: Paulist Press, 1961.

Mihanovich, Clement S., Gerald J. Schnepp, and John L. Thomas. *Marriage and the Family.* Milwaukee: Bruce Publishing Company, 1952.

347

O'Brien, John A. *Happy Marriage.* New York: Doubleday & Company, Inc., 1956.

O'Mahony, Patrick J. (ed.). *Catholics and Divorce.* New York: Thomas Nelson and Sons, 1960.

Pius XII, Pope. *Dear Newlyweds.* Translated by James F. Murray and Biance Murray. New York: Farrar, Straus & Company, 1961.

Popenoe, Paul and Cameron Disney. *Can This Marriage Be Saved?* New York: The Macmillan Company, 1960.

Sattler, Henry V. *Two to Get Ready.* Notre Dame: Fides Publishers, Inc., 1963.

Schnepp, Alfred F. and Gerald J. Schnepp. *To God Through Marriage.* Milwaukee: Bruce Publishing Company, 1958.

Thomas, John L. *Marriage and Rhythm.* Vista, California: The Newman Press, 1957.

Vanderveldt, J. and R. Odenwald. *Psychiatry and Catholicism.* New York: McGraw-Hill, Inc., 1952.

INDEX

INDEX

351